HOW TO BUILD
Proximity Detectors
and
Metal Locators

by JOHN POTTER SHIELDS

HOWARD W. SAMS & CO., INC.
THE BOBBS-MERRILL COMPANY, INC.
Indianapolis • New York

FIRST EDITION

FIRST PRINTING—SEPTEMBER, 1965

HOW TO BUILD PROXIMITY DETECTORS
AND
METAL LOCATORS

Library of Congress Catalog Card Number: 65-26262

Preface

Ever since its introduction some 40 years ago, the proximity detector has held a unique fascination for the experimenter. The ability to activate a lamp or other piece of electrical equipment without any physical contact seems almost magical, and it has led to the use of proximity detectors in countless displays and conversation pieces.

On the more practical side, proximity detectors are widely used in industry for such applications as safety devices, counting and sorting equipment, and surveillance. Other applications include burglar alarms, elevator controls, vibration analyzing equipment, thickness gauges, and many more.

A "first cousin" to the proximity detector, the metal locator is equally as fascinating. A form of proximity detector, the metal locator is generally designed to operate at considerably greater distances than the conventional proximity detector. Also, whereas the proximity detector is responsive to almost any mass, including the human body, metal locators are designed to respond only to metallic objects.

Metal locators are broken down into two basic classes: those that sense ferrous materials (such as iron and steel), and those that sense both ferrous and nonferrous materials (brass, zinc, copper, etc.).

Metal locators are used in industry for such applications as counting and sorting of small metal objects (e.g., nuts and bolts), determining the presence of foreign metallic materials in foods, etc. Military applications for metal locators include the famous mine detectors and locators. "Treasure" hunters find the metal locator handy in locating objects buried a few feet beneath the surface of the earth. Over water, metal locators are useful for finding such objects as outboard motors dropped from boat transoms, sunken tool boxes, and scores of other items.

In the following chapters, a number of practical, "de-bugged" circuits are described for building proximity detectors, metal locators, and theremins. The projects are broken down into two categories—elementary and advanced. The former units consist of one or two tubes or transistors. The circuits in the advanced category are more sophisticated and consist of three or more tubes or transistors. The final chapter explains the theremin, an electronic musical instrument that uses the beat-frequency proximity-detector principle.

JOHN POTTER SHIELDS

To my wife, Dorothy, without whose help and encouragement this book would not have been possible.

Contents

CHAPTER 5

CHAPTER 6

CHAPTER 7

Chapter 1

Proximity Detectors and Metal Locators

Since the introduction of proximity detectors in the 1920's, a number of different designs have been developed. The most popular circuits use the loaded-oscillator principle. In this circuit, the oscillator tank energy is shunted to ground by an external capacitance (sensing plate), and the resulting change in oscillator output is used to control a readout system. Other detectors use frequency shift, 60-cycle field excitation, beat-frequency conversion, f-m discriminator conversion, and the Doppler effect.

The metal locator is a "first cousin" to the proximity detector. While the proximity detector is generally assumed to be capable of sensing any "mass" (either metallic or nonmetallic), the metal locator is responsive only to metallic materials. The metal locators discussed in this book use the following principles: loaded-oscillator, beat-frequency conversion, coupled-magnetic field, moving-magnetic field, and the Hall effect. Since the metal locator has many of the same circuits as the proximity detector, it will be discussed later in this chapter, as well as in subsequent chapters.

The theremin is another "close relative" of the proximity detector. While it is used as a musical instrument instead of a means of detecting an object, the principle of operation is very similar to that of the proximity detector. It depends upon the proximity of the hand to the sensing plate for the production of the various tones. Because of this close relationship, the theremin is the subject of the final chapter of this book.

CAPACITY RELAYS

A basic proximity detector circuit called a "capacity relay" uses the loaded-oscillator principle. The "capacitive relay" is a descriptive

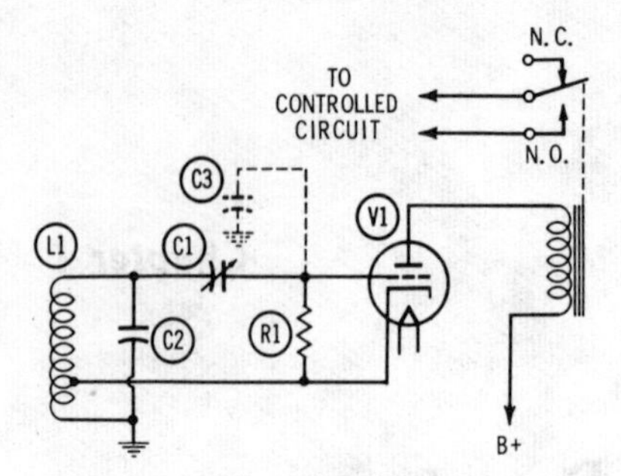

Fig. 1-1. A basic capacity-relay circuit.

term which is derived from theory of operation of this circuit. When properly designed, the capacity relay is simple and relatively foolproof.

Fig. 1-1 shows the basic capacity relay circuit—a Hartley oscillator with a relay connected in the plate circuit. In this class-C vacuum-tube oscillator circuit, the plate current of V1 is lowest when the circuit is oscillating and highest when it is not oscillating.

The circuit of the Fig. 1-1 differs from the conventional Hartley oscillator because grid-coupling capacitor C1 is adjustable. Therefore the amount of r-f energy flowing between V1 and the oscillator tank circuit (L1-C2) can be varied by adjusting C1. Notice that external capacitance C3 (between control grid of V1 and ground) is indicated by dashed lines.

With power applied to the circuit, assume that the initial external capacitance of C3 is negligible. Feedback capacitor C1 is adjusted so that sufficient r-f energy is coupled between V1 and the tank circuit (L1-C2) to sustain oscillations. Under these conditions, the plate current of V1 will be low, and the relay in the plate circuit will not be energized.

Assume that external capacitance C3 increases. This will decrease the capacitive reactance to ground, and a greater portion of the r-f signal appearing at the control grid of V1 will be bypassed to ground. Since the amplitude of r-f oscillations in the tank circuit (L1-C1) is

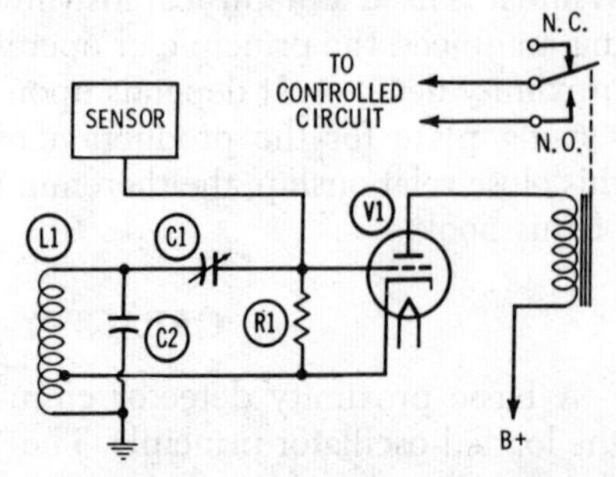

Fig. 1-2. A basic capacity-relay circuit with sensor.

decreased, the control grid bias on V1 (developed by the r-f oscillation) is reduced. The more positive control grid of V1 will cause the plate current to increase and energize the relay.

Fig. 1-2 shows the same circuit with a "sensing plate" (sensor) connected to the control grid of V1. When an object (such as a person's hand) approaches the sensing plate, the external capacitance between the control grid of V1 and ground will increase, reducing the amplitude of the oscillation in the oscillator tank. This increases the plate current through V1 and energizes the relay. Because the external capacitance "loads" the oscillator by bypassing the r-f signal to ground, this type of circuit is often referred to as a "loaded oscillator."

A-c Plate Supply Unit

There are numerous variations of the basic loaded-oscillator circuit. One variation is to operate the loaded oscillator with an a-c plate supply voltage. With this type of operation, the circuit goes into oscillation with every positive alternation of the applied a-c plate voltage. The circuit operates in the same way as when operated with a d-c plate supply, except that the oscillator operates only in "bursts" (when its plate-voltage alternation is positive). A capacitor is connected across the relay coil to smooth out the pulses of plate current through the relay coil.

Other types of loaded-oscillator capacity relays utilize one or more stages of amplification between the oscillator and the relay to increase sensitivity.

Frequency-Shift Unit

Another widely used type of "capacity relay" circuitry makes use of the fact that the addition of external capacitance across a tuned circuit will change its resonant frequency. The block diagram in Fig. 1-3 explains the operation of this type of circuit. Without an object close to the sensor, the variable-frequency oscillator frequency is adjusted to provide a zero output voltage from the frequency detector.

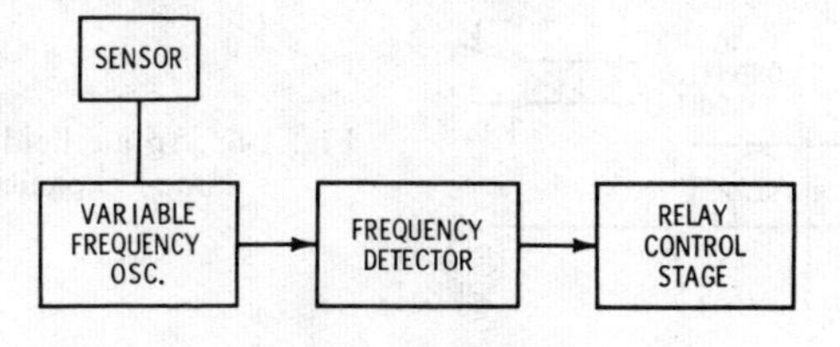

Fig. 1-3. A frequency-shift proximity detector.

When an object approaches the sensing plate, the oscillator changes frequency due to the increased capacitance across its tank coil. This shift in oscillator frequency is sensed by the frequency detector, which produces an output voltage that may be fed to a relay control stage.

A-c Field Amplifier

Still another type of capacity relay utilizes the electrostatic-electromagnetic field radiated by "open" power lines. As shown in block diagram (Fig. 1-4), the circuit consists of a high-gain audio-frequency amplifier, rectifier, and relay control stage. The sensor is connected to the input of the amplifier.

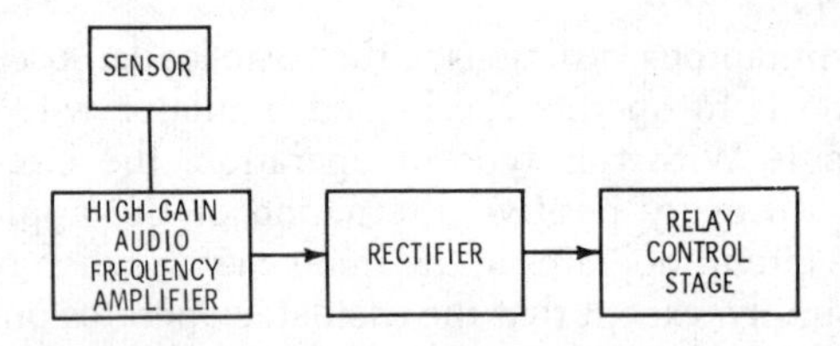

Fig. 1-4. An a-c field amplifier capacity relay.

The field radiated by the "open" electrical wiring induces an a-c signal into the sensing plate when it is touched by an object (such as a finger). This small a-c signal is amplified by the high-gain amplifier, rectified, and applied to the relay control stage.

A-c Field Control and Neon-Control Relay

Another type of a-c field-operated capacity relay circuit (Fig. 1-5) utilizes a gas discharge tube with the sensor connected to the control electrode. When a person touches the sensor, the a-c field from the power line induces a voltage on the control electrode of V1. The tube conducts and energizes a relay connected in the plate circuit. This approach has the advantage of extreme simplicity, and since no cur-

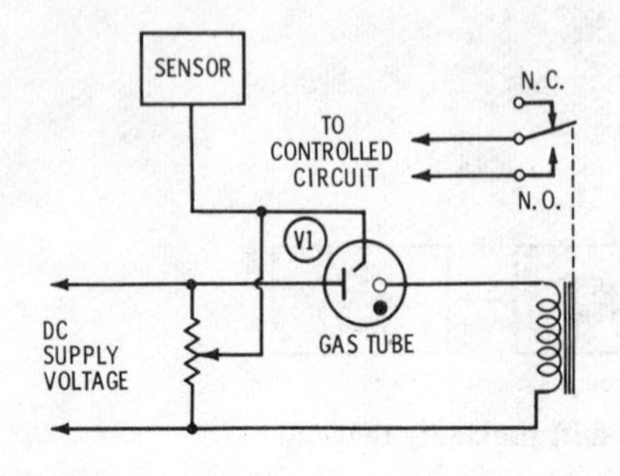

Fig. 1-5. An a-c field-control (neon lamp) capacity relay.

rent will be consumed until the gas is ionized, the circuit is also very economical.

DOPPLER-EFFECT PROXIMITY DETECTOR

Another major type of proximity detector operates on the Doppler-effect principle. The Doppler effect is the phenomenon whereby motion relative to the source of a signal will cause a change in its frequency. (The Doppler effect causes the change in pitch of the locomotive whistle when the train passes your immediate area.)

The block diagram in Fig. 1-6 shows the basic principle of the Doppler-effect proximity detector. A fixed-frequency oscillator supplies a high-frequency (ultrasonic) signal to a special type of speaker that floods the protected area with ultrasonic sound waves.

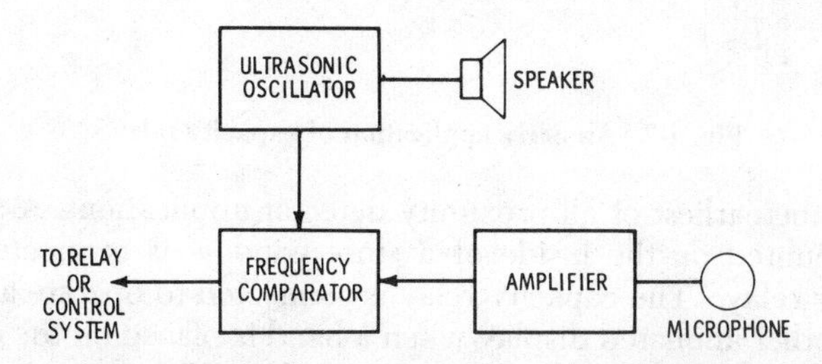

Fig. 1-6. A Doppler-effect proximity detector.

The high-frequency sound waves are picked up by a microphone, amplified, and fed to a frequency comparator. As long as there is no movement in the area covered by the sound "blanket," the sound picked up by the microphone will be exactly the same frequency as that emitted by the speaker, and there will be no output from the frequency comparator.

When an object moves in the area covered by the "sound blanket," the motion causes a slight shift in the frequency of the signal reaching the microphone. (This shift in frequency is due to the Doppler effect.) The frequency change is sensed by the frequency comparator, and an output voltage is produced. This voltage is applied to a relay control stage or other type of control system.

The Doppler-effect proximity detector has the advantages of being able to cover relatively large areas, and it is extremely sensitive to the movement of small objects.

PROXIMITY DETECTOR APPLICATIONS

There are numerous applications for proximity detectors, ranging from animated displays to industrial control circuits. Fig. 1-7 shows

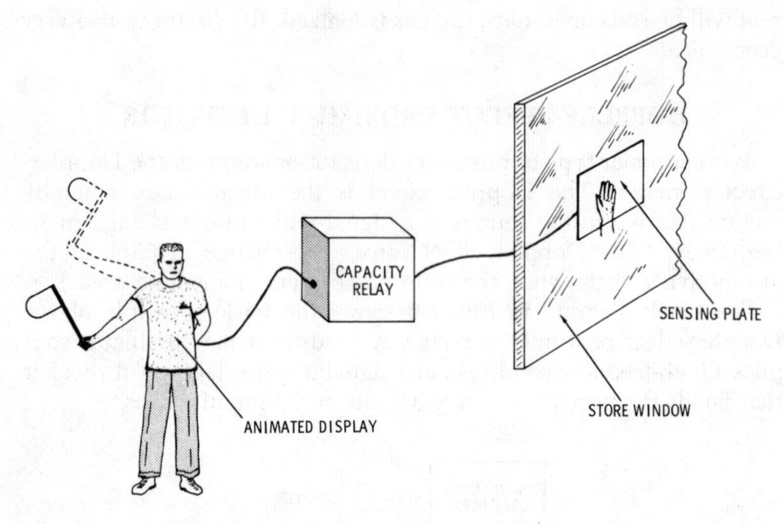

Fig. 1-7. An early application of capacity relay.

perhaps the earliest of all proximity detector applications. A sensing plate mounted on the inside of a store window is connected to a "capacity relay." The capacity relay is connected to operate a model train or other animated display when a hand is placed on the outside of the store window opposite the sensing plate. This setup was quite an attention-getter and resulted in the great popularity of the capacity-relay type of proximity detector in the '20's and '30's.

As time went on, the proximity detector and its applications became more complex. Industry found the proximity detector extremely useful in safety controls, level indicators, measuring devices, etc.

Liquid-Level Indicator

Fig. 1-8 shows the use of a proximity detector as a liquid-level indicator. In this application the proximity detector is used as part of an automatic feed system to keep the contents of the tank at a predetermined level. A sensing plate is mounted from the top of the tank so it will be a few inches above the liquid when the tank is properly filled. The sensing plate is connected to the proximity detector which produces an output voltage proportional to the distance between the liquid in the tank and the sensing plate.

The distance will increase between the sensing plate and liquid, as the liquid level in the tank is lowered. The resulting change in capacitance is converted (by the proximity detector) to an output signal. This signal energizes the system and starts the pump. As the tank fills, the capacitance between the liquid and sensing plate begins to decrease until it equals the original capacitance (distance

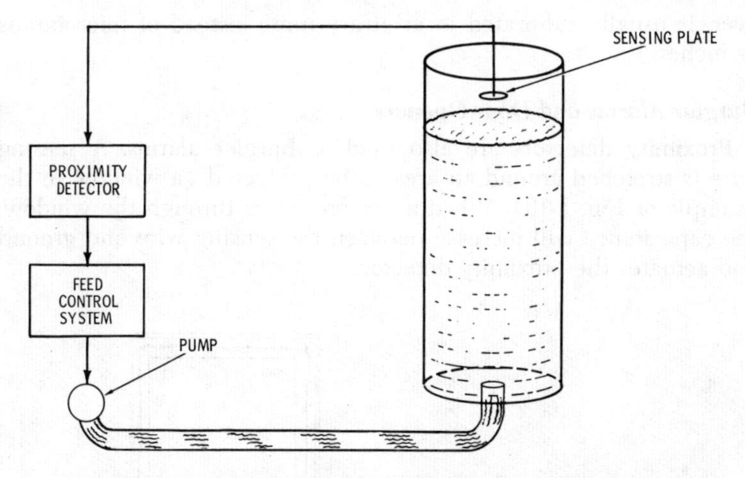

Fig. 1-8. Liquid level control by means of a proximity detector.

between sensing plate and liquid level). When this point is reached, the proximity detector signals the control system which stops the pump.

Thickness Gage

Fig. 1-9 shows how the proximity detector can be used as a thickness gage. The object is placed between two plates—one fixed and the other adjustable. These plates serve as the two plates of a capacitor, and the object serves as the dielectric for the capacitor. Thus, the thickness of the object determines the capacitance of the capacitor. As the thickness of the object is increased, the capacitance decreases; when the thickness is decreased, the capacitance increases. The two plates are connected to the proximity detector which actually measures the capacitance between the two plates. The meter on the detector, how-

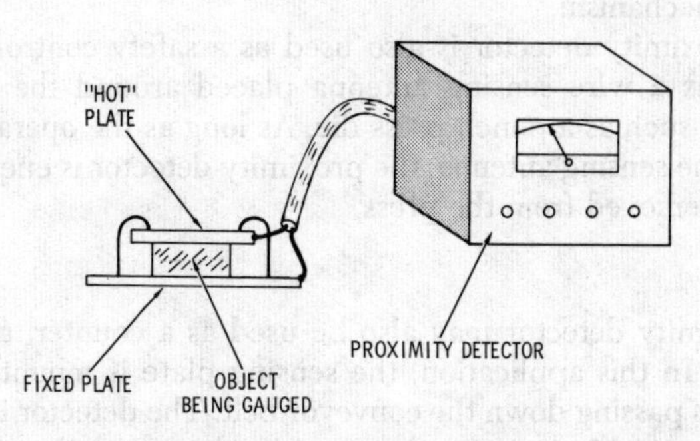

Fig. 1-9. Thickness measurement with a proximity detector.

ever, is usually calibrated in arbitrary units instead of microfarads or inches.

Burglar Alarms and Door Openers

Proximity detectors are also used as burgler alarms. A sensing wire is stretched around an area to be protected (a window in the example of Fig. 1-10). When a person enters through the window, the capacitance will increase between the sensing wire and ground and actuates the proximity detector.

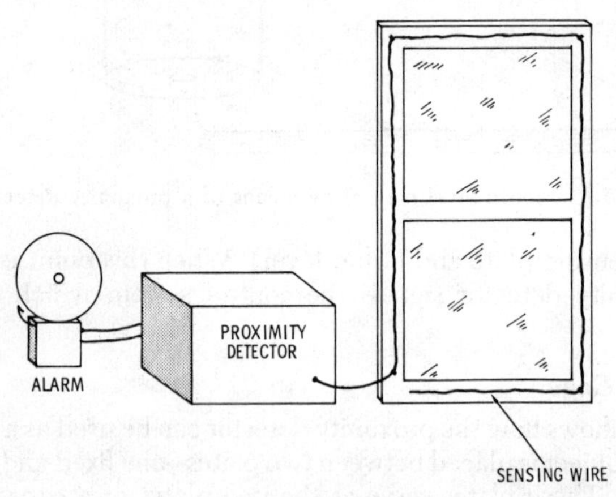

Fig. 1-10. A proximity detector as a burglar alarm.

Proximity detectors can also be used as "people counters" by stringing a wire around a building entrance. In this instance, the relay in the proximity detector could actuate a electromechanical counter. Automatic-door operation can be obtained by connecting the output of the proximity detector to an electrically operated door-opening mechanism.

The proximity detector is also used as a safety control. A typical control has a wire sensing antenna placed around the area to be protected, such as a punch press die. As long as the operator's hands are near the sensing antenna, the proximity detector is energized, and power is removed from the press.

Counters

A proximity detector may also be used as a counter, as shown in Fig. 1-11. In this application, the sensing plate is mounted close to the objects passing down the conveyor belt. The detector is energized each time an object passes the sensing plate, and the output from the detector is fed to a electromechanical counter.

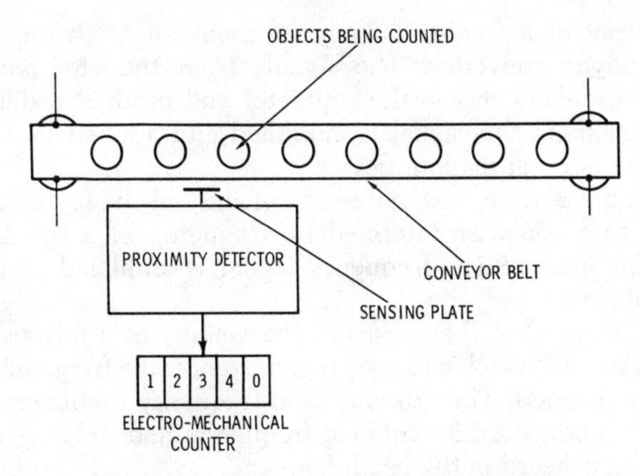

Fig. 1-11. A proximity detector as a counter.

This type of proximity counter provides superior results when compared to the more conventional photocell counter in applications where the line of sight of the photocell optical system can be obstructed. The proximity counter also can sense transparent objects which the photocell counter would "see" right through.

METAL LOCATORS

Metal locators are divided into two basic classes. One type will only sense ferrous (iron or steel) materials, and the other type will respond to both ferrous and nonferrous (copper, brass, zinc, tin, etc.) objects.

Beat-Frequency Locator

The most conventional type of metal locator operates on the beat, or heterodyne, principle (Fig. 1-12). When the search coil is connected to an r-f oscillator a change in the search coil inductance caused by nearby ferrous objects will shift the oscillator frequency. The output from this variable-frequency oscillator (vfo) is fed to a heterodyne converter.

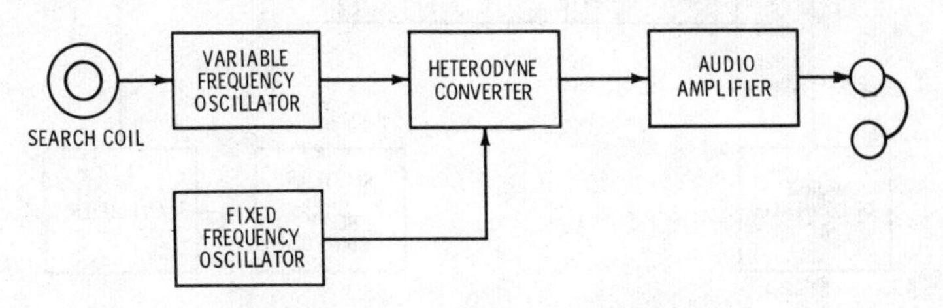

Fig. 1-12. A beat-frequency metal locator.

The output of a fixed-frequency r-f oscillator is also applied to the heterodyne converter. The signals from the vfo- and fixed-frequency oscillator mix in the converter and produce a difference-frequency signal. This signal is amplified and applied to a pair of headphones or other readout device.

Without any ferrous material in the vicinity of the search coil, the vfo is set to produce an intermediate frequency of a few hundred cycles. This intermediate-frequency signal is amplified and fed to the headphones.

When the search coil approaches the vicinity of a ferrous object, the inductance of search coil is changed. Hence, the frequency of the vfo is also changed. The vfo and fixed-frequency oscillator outputs combine to produce a different beat-frequency, and a change in pitch of the signal is heard in the headphones.

The principle of the beat-frequency metal locator is similar to the frequency-shift proximity detector described earlier (Fig. 1-3), except that the inductance of the oscillator tank circuit is changed rather than the capacitance. Also, a pair of headphones is substituted for the rectifier and relay control stage used in the frequency-shift proximity detector. This detector will also respond to nonferrous metals with reduced sensitivity.

Coupled-Field Locator

Fig. 1-13 is a block diagram of another type of metal locator. This type of locator operates on the principle of magnetic coupling between two inductances.

Coil A is supplied with low-frequency a-c current, and it generates an alternating magnetic field. A second coil (B) is located so that its magnetic field is at right angles to the magnetic field of coil A. The output of coil B is amplified and applied to a rectifier and relay

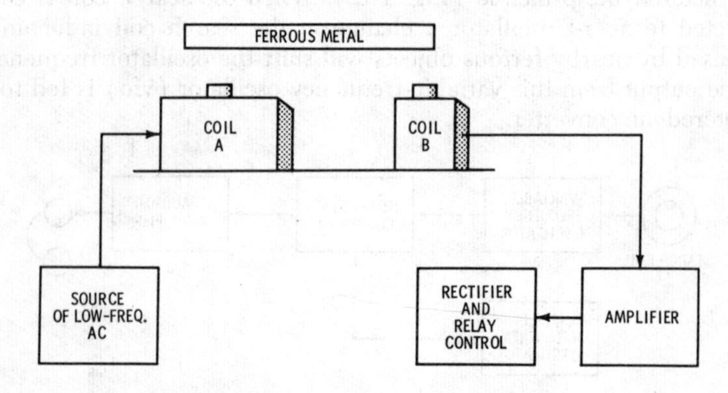

Fig. 1-13. A coupled-field metal locator.

control stage. In the absence of any ferrous material between coils A and B, the magnetic field radiates from coil A, inducing a small current in coil B. The amplitude of this current is insufficient to energize the relay.

When a piece of ferrous material approaches space between A and B, an increased amount of magnetic flux is coupled from coil A to coil B. The amount of current induced in coil B increases and, after amplification, energizes the relay.

Although a relatively large metal object is required before sufficient current will be produced to operate the relay, there are many applications where this circuit can be used. It offers the advantage of being relatively simple and rugged.

Ferrous-Metal Separator

The "nonelectronic" metal locator (Fig. 1-14), which is perhaps the simplest of all metal locators, consists of only a magnetic drum. This type of metal locator is used to sort out ferrous metal from such raw materials as coal, flour, etc.

The material is carried on a conveyor belt to the drum; it then passes over the magnetic drum. Any ferrous objects will be attracted and held to the drum, while the nonferrous objects will pass over the drum. This type of detector is widely used in coal mines, flour mills, etc.

Changing-Field Locator

Still another type of metal locator (Fig. 1-15) operates when a ferrous object, such as a tin can, passes close to a sensor (pickup coil).

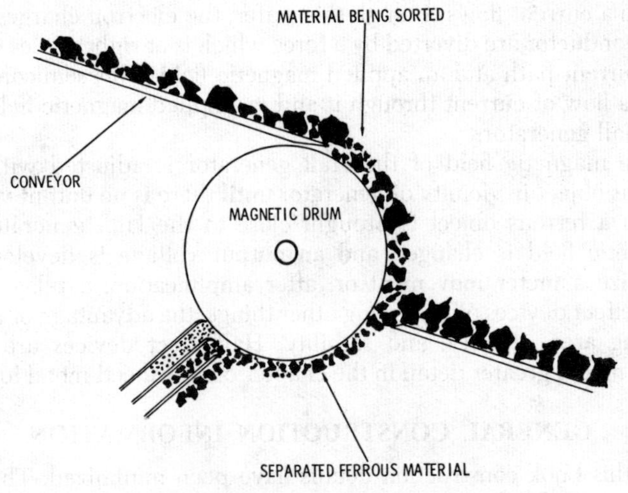

Fig. 1-14. A ferrous-metal separator.

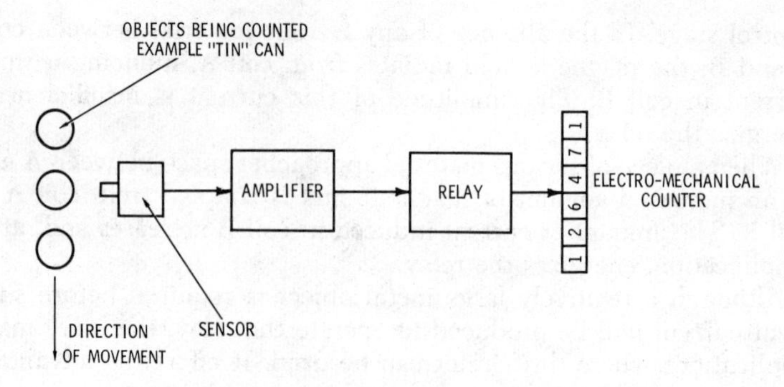

Fig. 1-15. A changing magnetic-field metal locator.

The basic components of this type of metal locator are the sensor, amplifier, relay, and counter circuit. The sensor consists of many turns of wire wound on a permanent-magnet core. The coil of the sensor is connected to the input of a high-gain a-f amplifier. The output of this amplifier is fed to the relay and counter circuits.

A current impulse is generated in the sensor when magnetic lines of force from the sensor are cut by the passage of a tin can. The amplitude of the impulse is increased by the amplifier to operate an electromechanical counter. Since this locator responds only to moving ferrous objects, it can be located in the vicinity of fixed metallic objects.

Hall-Effect Locators

In this metal locator a voltage (for an indicator or relay) is developed across the width of a thin wafer of semiconductor material. When a current flows through this wafer, the electron charges in the semiconductor are diverted by a force which is at right angles to both the current path and an applied magnetic field. This semiconductor with a flow of current through it and its applied magnetic field form the Hall generator.

The magnetic field of the Hall generator is adjusted without a ferrous object in vicinity of generator until there is no output voltage. When a ferrous object is brought close to the Hall generator, the magnetic field is changed and an output voltage is developed to energize a meter movement or, after amplification, a relay. These Hall-effect devices offer, among other things, the advantage of a small sensing area, rigidity, and stability. Hall-effect devices are to be examined in greater detail in the chapter on advanced metal locators.

GENERAL CONSTRUCTION INFORMATION

In this book construction details have been minimized. This permits greater flexibility in the layout of each project. The photographs and pictorial drawings on most of these projects are offered only as a guide. Close attention to the instructions given in the text along with the photographs and pictorial drawings should be sufficient to construct any of these units.

Only the electrical components are included in the parts lists. A tolerance of ±10% is allowed on all resistor values. The working voltage of capacitors should not be less than 200V dc for the vacuum tube circuits and 25V dc for the transistor circuits. A spst-contact relay may be substituted, when an extra set of contacts is not required, for the spdt-contact relay.

The layout of the component mounting holes on a metal chassis should be made on a stiff piece of cardboard. A letter file folder is a good source of layout material. Cut the cardboard to match the top of chassis. After careful location of the parts on this layout, it is fastened to the top of chassis with tape. The center of holes can be located from this layout with a center punch. On chassis that use perforated phenolic board, the terminal tie points can be brass paper eyelets.

Fig. 1-16 shows a suggested method of attaching the sensing plate to a proximity detector with an unshielded lead. A small hole is drilled in one corner of the plate, and a machine screw is placed through the hole. The lead from the proximity detector is wrapped around the screw, the nut attached, and the screw is tightened.

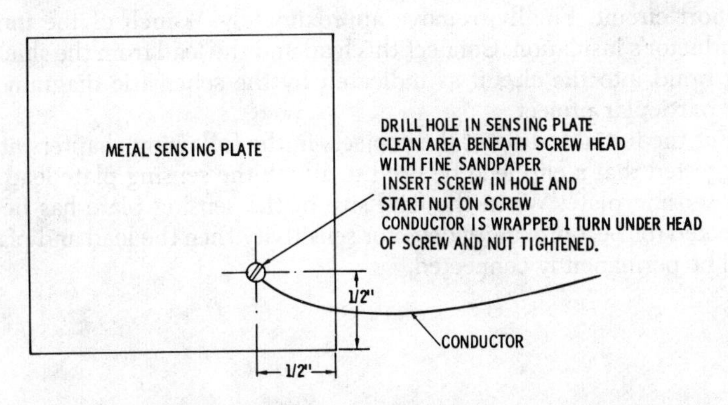

Fig. 1-16. Connecting an unshielded lead to the sensing plate.

The correct method of attaching a shielded cable between a sensing plate and proximity detector is shown in Fig. 1-17. Both the insulation and shield braid are removed from the end of cable that connects to the sensing plate. Only the inner conductor is connected to the sensing plate. The opposite end of the shielded cable, that connects to the proximity detector, is prepared as follows: The plastic jacket

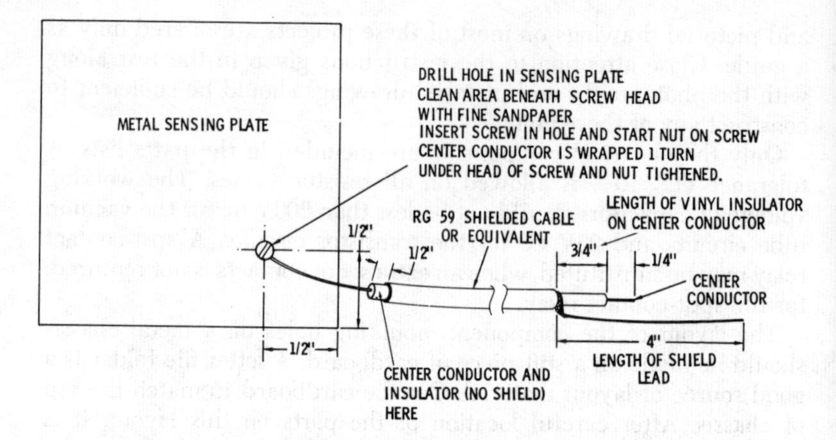

Fig. 1-17. Connecting a shielded cable to the sensing plate.

is removed to a point approximately one inch back from the end of the cable. The interlaced braid of shield is unlaced and this length of braid is twisted into a single stranded bundle. This bundle is wrapped with several turns of solid copper No. 18 or No. 20 wire and this joint is then soldered. About 4-inches of the end of this shield lead is left for connection to the proximity detector. When soldering to the braid, avoid applying excessive heat as this may melt the insulation between the shielding braid and center conductor, causing a short circuit. Finally, remove approximately ¼-inch of the inner conductor's insulation. Connect this lead and the lead from the shielding braid into the circuit as indicated by the schematic diagram of the particular project.

For the initial testing of the projects in the following chapters, it is suggested that a clip lead be used to attach the sensing plate lead to the sensing plate. When the final size of the sensing plate has been selected for best proximity detector sensitivity then the lead and plate can be permanently connected.

Chapter 2

Elementary Proximity Detectors

The proximity detectors in this chapter will have various degrees of sensitivity, the simpler circuits require that the object touch the sensing plate and the more complex circuits require that the object only approach the sensing plate. It will be shown how these circuits can be modified so that they will remain closed after the object has approached and left the vicinity of the sensor. Another modification requires that the object again approach the sensor to recycle the detection process. This last function would be required to operate a light switch, electric motors, etc. Also proximity detectors using both the loaded oscillator and the 60-cycle field-excitation principles will be discussed.

SINGLE-STAGE LOADED-OSCILLATOR TOUCHSWITCH

To get started in this proximity detector game, we will try our hand at perhaps the simplest of all proximity detector circuits—a single-stage touchswitch. A touchswitch is a relatively low sensitivity proximity detector. The object must be very close to or actually touch the sensor before the detector will operate. The circuit in Fig. 2-1 demonstrates the principle of the loaded-oscillator type of proximity detector. Although this detector has less sensitivity than the more advanced circuits described later, it has a number of useful applications.

Circuit Description

Fig. 2-1 is the schematic of the touchswitch. V1 (6AQ5), tank coil L1, feedback capacitor C1, and grid-leak resistor R1 form the basic oscillator circuit. Relay K1 is energized when sufficient plate current flows through its windings.

Feedback capacitor C1 is adjusted until oscillations are sustained without an object in the vicinity of the sensing plate or sensor. Under

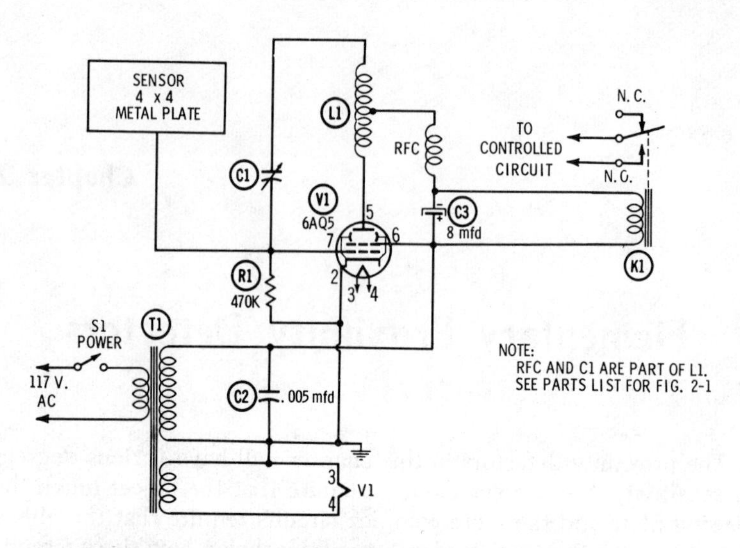

Fig. 2-1. A single-stage, loaded-oscillator touchswitch circuit.

Parts List for Fig. 2-1

Item	Description
C1	Capacitor, adjustable (part of L1)
C2	Capacitor, .005 mfd, 400v dc
C3	Capacitor, 8 mfd, 150v, electrolytic
K1	Relay, 5000 ohm d-c coil, spdt contacts, Potter Brumfield RS5D or equiv.
L1	Coil, capacity-operated relay, J. W. Miller Type 695 or equiv.
RFC	Choke, r-f (part of L1)
R1	Resistor, 470K ½ watt
S1	Switch, toggle, spst
T1	Transformer, power, pri. 117v, sec. 125v @ 50 ma, sec. 6.3V @ 2 amp
V1	Tube, 6AQ5

this quiescent condition, the plate current of V1 will not be sufficient to energize the relay in the plate circuit of V1.

When an object approaches the sensor, the capacitance increases between the sensor and ground and bypasses some feedback energy from the oscillating circuit. The amplitude of oscillations in the tank circuit will decrease; this decreases the bias on V1 causing the plate current of V1 to increase until relay K1 is energized.

The plate and screen grid voltages are supplied directly from the secondary of power (isolation) transformer T1. The oscillations are re-started each time the plate of V1 becomes positive with respect to its cathode. The plate current pulses will supply the indictive "kick" in L1 to re-start oscillations when the object is removed from the proximity of the sensor.

Construction

The touchswitch is assembled on a small aluminum chassis as shown in Fig. 2-2. The isolation transformer (T1), oscillator coil (L1), tube (V1), relay (K1), and terminal board are mounted on the top of the chassis and all other components underneath the chassis. The placement of the electronic parts is not critical. A different size chassis may also be used. The only requirement is to keep the leads reasonably short, particularly in the oscillator section. The completed touchswitch is shown in Fig. 2-3.

Some component substitution is permissible, so you can take advantage of your junk box. For example, a 6V6, 6F6, or 6K6 may be substituted for the 6AQ5; however, it will be necessary to substitute an octal socket for the 7-pin miniature socket used for the 6AQ5. R1 may be any available value between 1 and 10 megs—the higher values will give more sensitivity. C1 may range from .005 to 0.1 mfd. Since this circuit functions only on positive alternation of a-c plate voltage, this circuit is self rectifying and no a-c voltage is developed across C3. Therefore, C3 may be any value between 4 and 20 mfd as its only purpose is to prevent the relay from chattering.

Adjustment

After completing the touchswitch, check it carefully for any wiring errors. Connect a sensing plate (sensor), made from a piece of metal or aluminum foil, to the sensor terminal (grid of 6AQ5, Pin 7). The initial plate or foil should be made approximately four inches square.

With power applied to the unit, adjust the capacity of C1 to its maximum value (screw turned to its maximum clockwise position). This will produce maximum amplitude of oscillations, and the relay will open. Without an object in close proximity to the sensor, reduce the capacity of C1 by turning the screw in a counterclockwise direction until the relay energizes. Then slowly increase the capacity of C1 until the relay just opens. Now touching the sensing plate with a finger should cause the relay to close.

Because of the simplicity of this circuit, the proximity detection range is limited. The most sensitive operation is obtained when C1 is adjusted to the point where the relay just opens. Any further increase in the capacity of C1 will decrease the sensitivity of unit. Increasing the size of the sensing plate will also increase the sensitivity of the touchswitch. If the sensing plate is made too large, however, the circuit will not oscillate for any setting of C1. Sensitivity can also

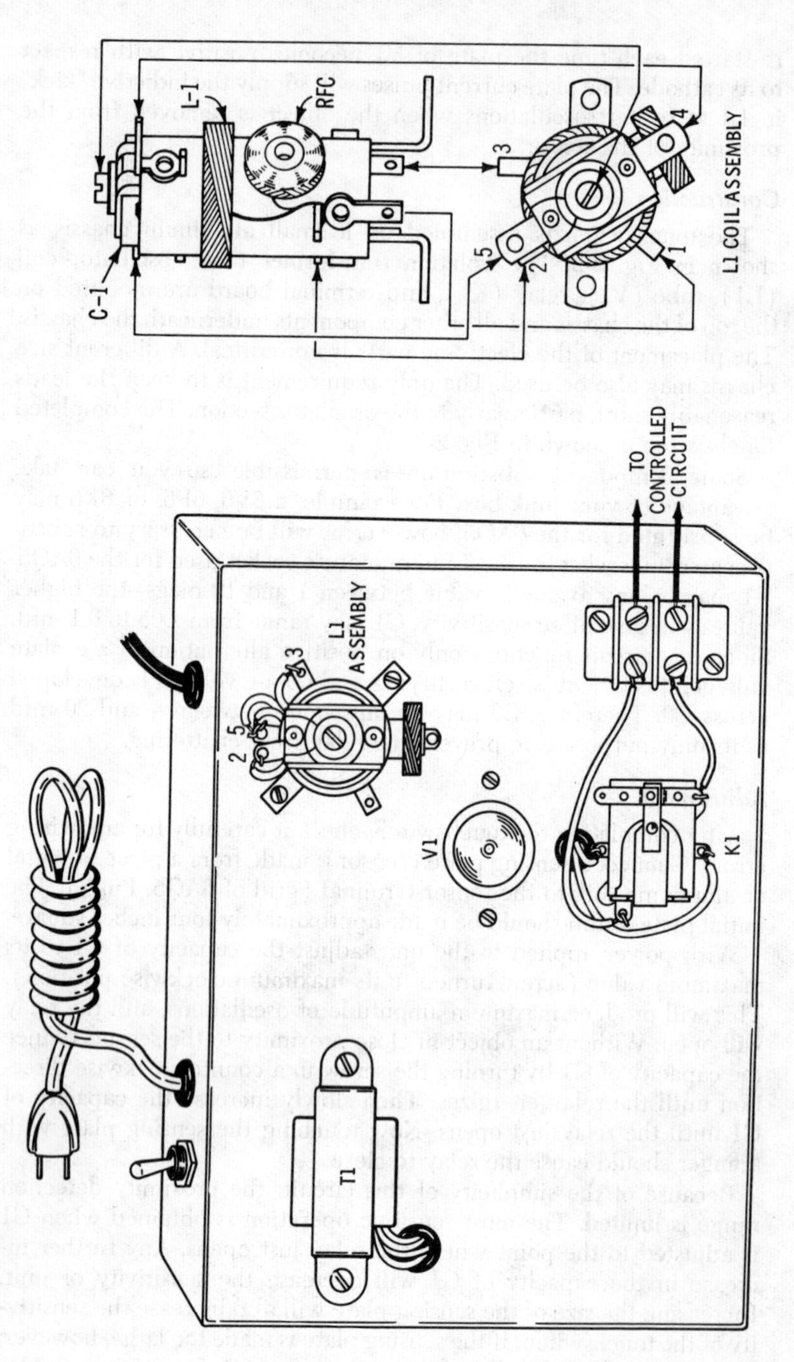

Fig. 2-2. Pictorial

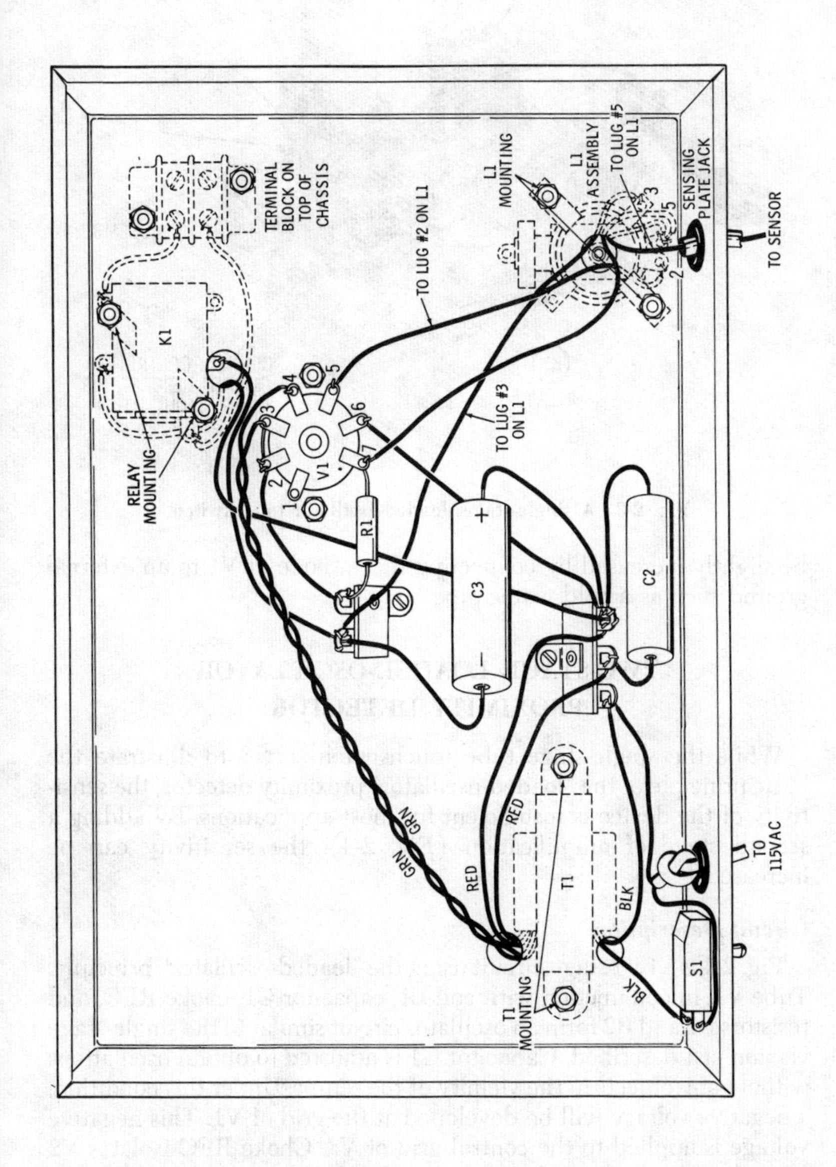

diagram for Fig. 2-1.

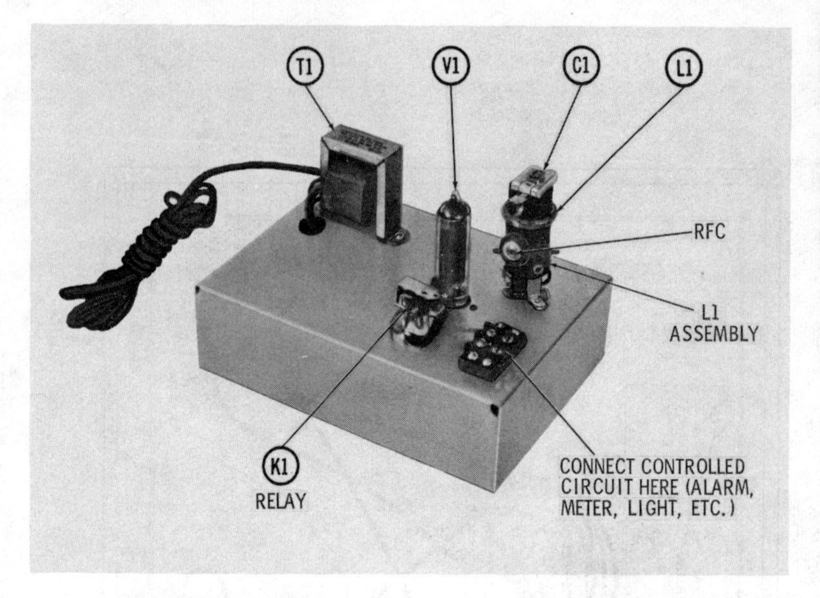

Fig. 2-3. A single-stage, loaded-oscillator touchswitch.

be slightly increased by connecting the cathode of V1 to an external ground such as a cold water pipe.

TWO-STAGE LOADED-OSCILLATOR PROXIMITY DETECTOR

While the single-stage tube touchswitch serves to illustrate the basic principle of the "loaded-oscillator" proximity detector, the sensitivity of the device is insufficient for most applications. By adding a second stage of amplification (Fig. 2-4), the sensitivity can be increased.

Circuit Description

Fig. 2-4 is a two-stage circuit using the "loaded-oscillator" principle. Tube V1, in conjunction with coil L1, capacitor C1, choke RFC, and resistors R1 and R2 form an oscillator circuit similar to the single-stage version just described. Capacitor C1 is adjusted to obtain oscillations without any objects in the vicinity of the sensor. Under this condition, a negative voltage will be developed at the grid of V1. This negative voltage is applied to the control grid of V2. Choke RFC isolates V2 from the r-f voltage at the control grid of V1.

The amplitude of the oscillations is reduced when an object approaches the sensing plate, and this will reduce the negative grid

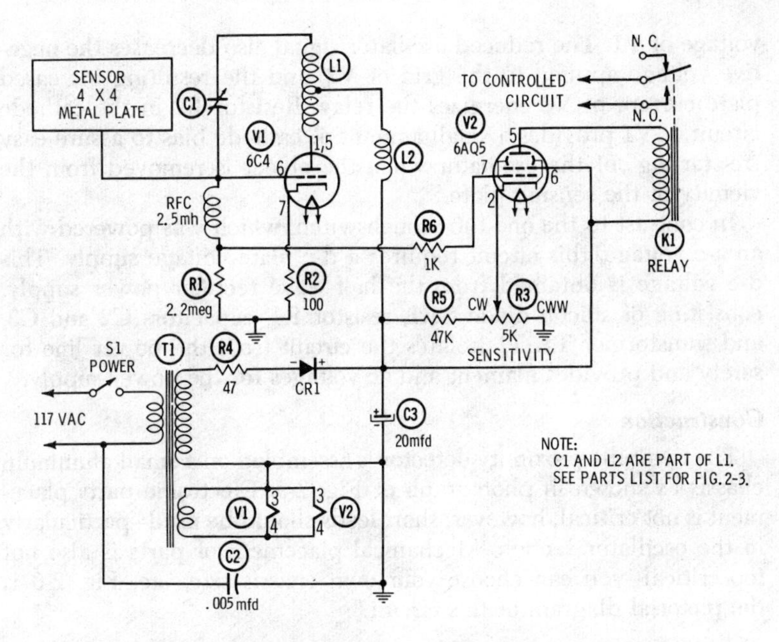

Fig. 2-4. A two-stage, loaded-oscillator, proximity detector.

Parts List for Fig. 2-4

Item	Description
C1	Capacitor, adjustable (part of L1)
C2	Capacitor, .005 mfd, 400v
C3	Capacitor, 20 mfd, 150v, electrolytic
CR1	Rectifier, silicon, 1N2484 or equiv.
K1	Relay, 5000 ohm d-c coil, spdt contact, Potter Brumfield RS5D or equiv.
L1	Coil capacity-operated relay, J. W. Miller Type 695, or equiv.
L2	Coil (part of L1)
RFC	Choke, r-f, 2.5 mh
R1	Resistor, 2.2 megohm, ½ watt
R2	Resistor, 100 ohm, ½ watt
R3	Potentometer, 5K ohm, 2 watt
R4	Resistor, 47 ohm, ½ watt
R5	Resistor, 47K ohm, ½ watt
R6	Resistor, 1K ohm, ½ watt
RFC	Choke, r-f (part of L1)
S1	Switch, spst, toggle
T1	Transformer, pri. 117v, sec. 125v @ 50 ma, 6.3v @ 2 amp
V1	Tube, 6C4
V2	Tube, 6AQ5

voltage of V1. The reduced oscillator signal also decreases the negative voltage applied to the grid of V2, and the resulting increased plate current of V2 energizes the relay. Resistor R2 in the cathode circuit of V1 provides a small amount of cathode bias to assure easy "re-starting" of the oscillator when the object is removed from the vicinity of the sensing plate.

In contrast to the one-tube touchswitch, which was powered with an a-c voltage, this circuit requires a d-c plate-voltage supply. This d-c voltage is obtained from the half-wave rectifier power supply, consisting of silicon diode CR1, resistor R4, capacitors C2 and C3, and transformer T1. T1 isolates the circuit from the power line for safety and provides filament and ac voltages for the power supply.

Construction

The two-tube proximity detector is assembled on a small aluminum chassis as shown in photograph of Fig. 2-5. Electronic parts placement is not critical; however, short leads should be used—particularly in the oscillator section. Mechanical placement of parts is also not too critical—you can choose your own chassis size, etc. Fig. 2-6 is the pictorial diagram of this circuit.

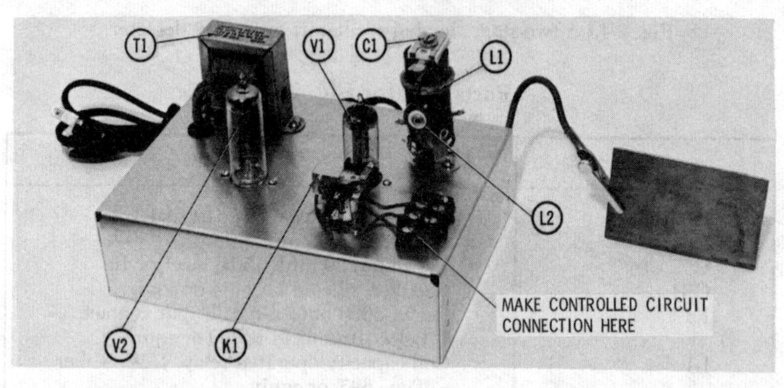

Fig. 2-5. A two-stage, loaded-oscillator proximity detector.

Component parts can be substituted as follows: tube V1 may be a 6J5 or ½ of a 12AU7, R1 (1 to 10 megohm), R3 (1 to 5 kilohm), RFC (2.5 to 5 millihenry). The tube socket must be changed when an octal tube is substituted for a miniature tube.

Adjustment

Connect a sensing plate to the control grid of V1 (6C4, Pin 6)—a good size to start with is a 4-inch square piece of aluminum foil or sheet metal. Set sensitivity control R3 midway between its minimum and maximum resistance settings. With power applied, increase the

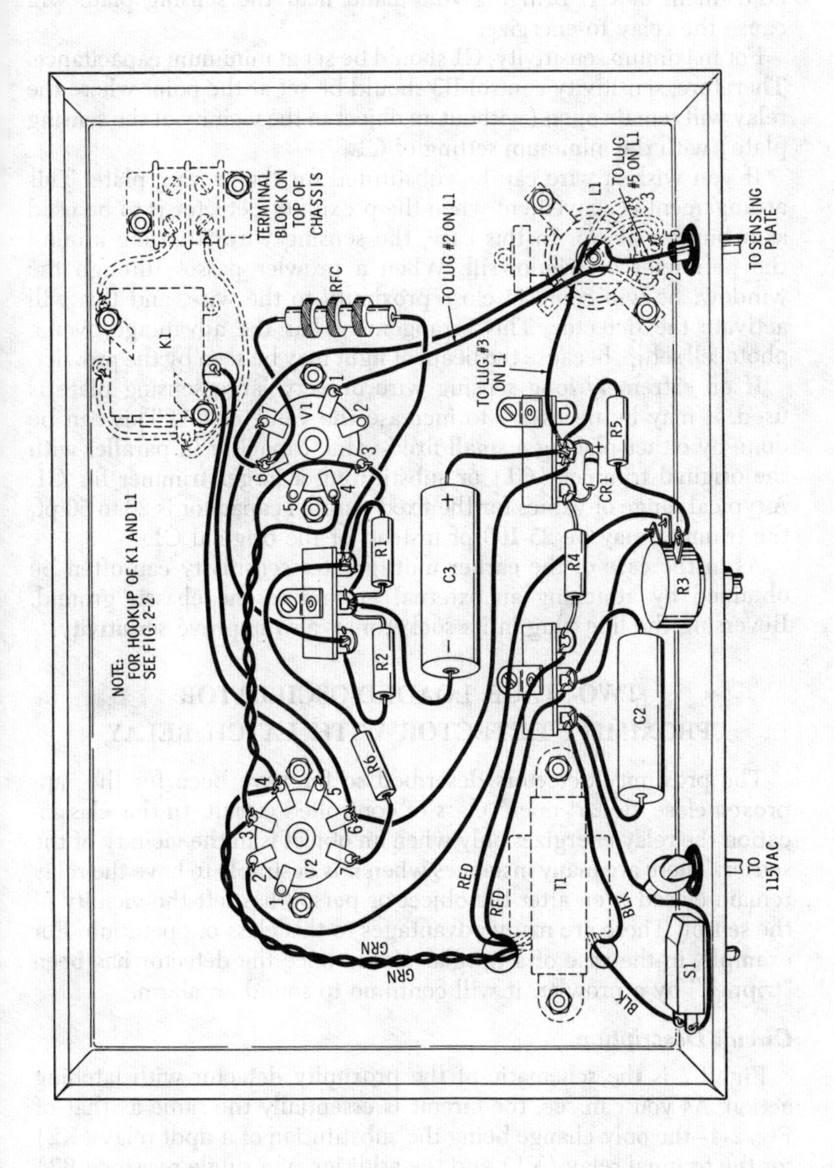

Fig. 2-6. Pictorial diagram for Fig. 2-4.

capacitance of C1 until relay K1 opens; then decrease it until the relay closes. Again, increase the capacitance of C1 until the relay just opens. Optimum operation of the relay is achieved by careful adjustment of C1. Bringing your hand near the sensing plate will cause the relay to energize.

For maximum sensitivity, C1 should be set at minimum capacitance. Therefore, sensitivity control R3 should be set at the point where the relay will remain open (without an object in the vicinity of the sensing plate) with the minimum setting of C1.

If you wish, a wire can be substituted for the sensing plate. This arrangement is convenient when the proximity detector is to be used as a burglar alarm. In this case, the sensing wire is strung around the perimeter of windowsill. When a prowler passes through the window, he will come in close proximity to the wire, and this will activate the detector. This arrangement has the advantage over a photocell setup, because the beam of light may be seen by the prowler.

If an extremely long sensing wire or very large sensing plate is used, it may be necessary to increase the value of C1. This can be done by either placing a small fixed-value capacitor in parallel with the original trimmer (C1) or substituting a larger trimmer for C1. A typical range of values for the fixed parallel capacitor is 20 to 50 pf, the trimmer may be 25-100 pf instead of the original C1.

As in the case of the earlier unit, greater sensitivity can often be obtained by attaching an external ground to the chassis ground. Reversing the line plug in its socket may also improve sensitivity.

TWO-STAGE LOADED-OSCILLATOR PROXIMITY DETECTOR WITH LATCH RELAY

The proximity detectors described so far have been for the "approach close, depart open" class of controlled circuit. In this classification the relay energizes only when an object is in the vicinity of the sensor. There are many instances when it is desirable to have the relay remain closed even after the object or person has left the vicinity of the sensor. There are many advantages to this class of operation. For example, in the case of a burglar alarm, once the detector has been "tripped" by a prowler, it will continue to sound an alarm.

Circuit Description

Fig. 2-7 is the schematic of the proximity detector with latching action. As you can see, the circuit is essentially the same as that of Fig. 2-4—the only change being the substitution of a dpdt relay (K2) for the original relay (K1) and the addition of a single resistor (R7) and a normally-closed, push-button switch (S2). Fig. 2-8 is a pictorial diagram that shows the completed chassis.

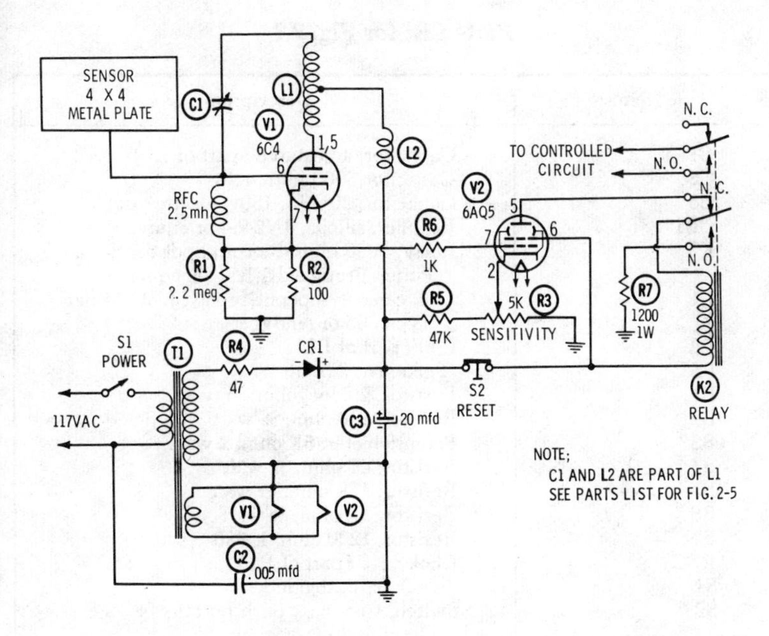

Fig. 2-7. A two-stage, loaded-oscillator proximity detector with latching relay.

When the circuit is at rest, the plate current of V2 flows through the normally-closed contacts of K2, the K2 coil, and the normally-closed reset switch to the power supply. When an object approaches the sensor, the negative grid bias of V2 decreases, and the plate current of the tube increases. The increased plate current energizes relay K2 and moves the armature to the normally open contact. This now connects the relay coil between B+ and ground through limiting resistor R7. This resistor allows sufficient current to pass through the relay coil to keep the relay energized. Since the relay coil is now connected directly between B+ and ground (through the limiting resistor), it will remain closed without an object near the sensing plate.

To reset the relay for normal operation, the reset switch is pushed to open the relay circuit. This breaks the circuit between B+ and ground, and the armature of K2 returns to the normally-closed contact. This action restores the plate voltage to V2, and the circuit is at rest, ready for the next cycle.

TWO-STAGE LOADED-OSCILLATOR PROXIMITY DETECTOR WITH THYRATRON RELAY CONTROL

While the preceding circuit offers good sensitivity, there is still room for improvement. By substituting a thyratron for the vacuum-

Parts List for Fig. 2-7

Item	Description
C1	Capacitor, adjustable (part of L1)
C2	Capacitor, .005 mfd, 400v
C3	Capacitor, 20 mfd, 150v, electrolytic
CR1	Rectifier, silicon, 1N2484 or equiv.
K2	Relay, 5000 ohm d-c coil, dpdt contacts, Potter Brumfield FR11 or equiv.
L1	Coil, capacity-operated relay, J. W. Miller Type 695 or equiv.
L2	Coil (part of L1)
RFC	Choke, r-f, 2.5 mh
R1	Resistor, 2.2 megohm, ½ watt
R2	Resistor, 100 ohm, ½ watt
R3	Potentiometer, 5K ohm, 2 watt
R4	Resistor, 47 ohm, ½ watt
R5	Resistor, 47K ohm, ½ watt
R6	Resistor, 1K ohm, ½ watt
R7	Resistor, 1200 ohm, 1 watt
RFC	Choke, r-f (part of L1)
S1	Switch, spst, toggle
S2	Switch, spst, n.c., push button, Grayhill 30-2 or equiv.
T1	Transformer, pri. 117v, sec. 125v @ 50 ma, 6.3v @ 2 amp
V1	Tube, 6C4
V2	Tube, 6AQ5

type tube in relay control stage V2, it is possible to achieve increased sensitivity.

Before describing this circuit, we will take a moment to review the operation of a thyratron. Unlike a conventional "hard" vacuum tube, the thyratron is filled with an inert gas, such as neon or argon. With plate and filament voltages applied to a thyratron and the control grid maintained at a few volts negative with respect to cathode, no current will flow between the cathode and plate. When the grid bias reaches zero, the gas within the thyratron will ionize or "fire", thus resulting in a heavy flow of current through the tube. Once this flow of current has started, the control grid will lose all control, and the plate voltage supply of the thyratron must be interrupted to stop the flow of current through the tube. This loss of plate current control is in contrast to the vacuum tube where the grid has complete control of the flow of current. Also, the thyratron has only two operating states, "full off" or "full on" plate current, where as the plate current of vacuum tube may have any value ranging from zero to maximum.

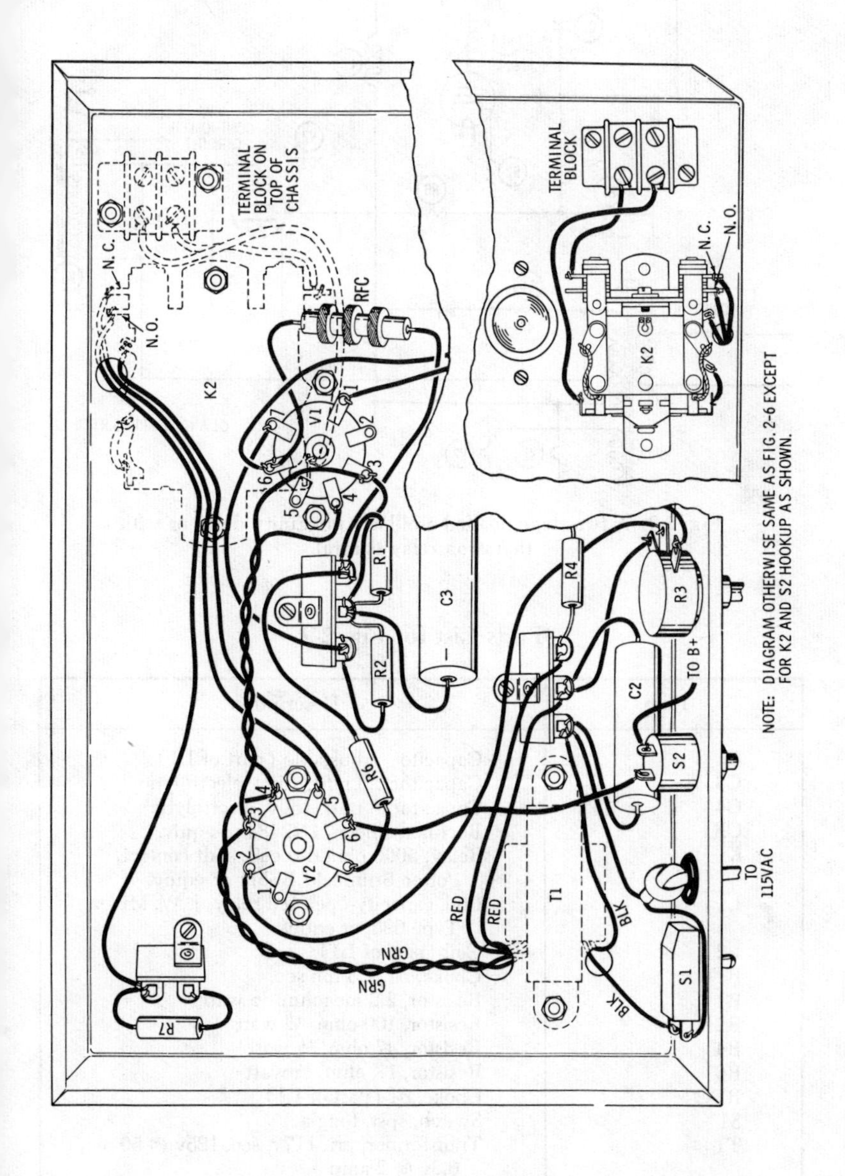

Fig. 2-8. Pictorial diagram for Fig. 2-7.

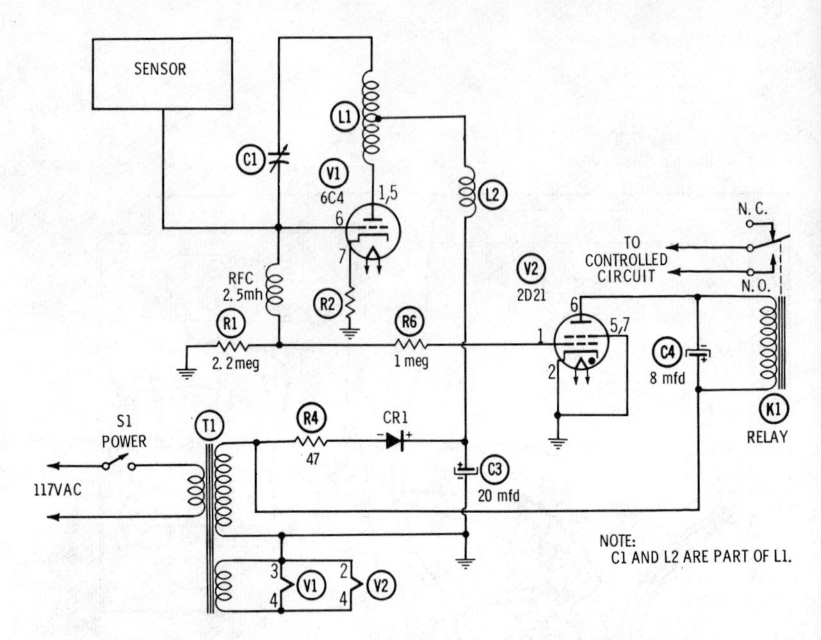

Fig. 2-9. A two-stage, loaded-oscillator proximity detector with thyratron relay control.

Parts List for Fig. 2-9

Item	Description
C1	Capacitor, adjustable (part of L1)
C3	Capacitor, 20 mfd, 150v, electrolytic
C4	Capacitor, 8 mfd, 150v, electrolytic
CR1	Rectifier, silicon, 1N2484 or equiv.
K1	Relay, 5000 ohm d-c coil, spdt contact, Potter Brumfield RS5D or equiv.
L1	Coil, capacity-operated relay, J. W. Miller Type 695, or equiv.
L2	Coil (part of L1)
RFC	Choke, r-f, 2.5 mh sec.
R1	Resistor, 2.2 megohm, ½ watt
R2	Resistor, 100 ohm, ½ watt
R4	Resistor, 47 ohm, ½ watt
R6	Resistor, 1K ohm, ½ watt
RFC	Choke, r-f (part of L1)
S1	Switch, spst, toggle
T1	Transformer, pri. 117v, sec. 125v @ 50 ma, 6.3v @ 2 amp
V1	Tube, 6C4
V2	Tube, thyratron, 2D21

Circuit Description

Now we will take a look at the circuit (Fig. 2-9). The "loaded-oscillator" stage (V1) is identical to the same stage of Fig. 2-7. The basic circuit change is the substitution of a thyratron (2D21) for the vacuum tube (6AQ5) in the relay control circuit.

When the circuit is at rest (without an object in the vicinity of the sensing plate), the negative voltage on the grid of V2 is developed by the oscillations in the V1 tank circuit. This negative voltage is sufficient to keep the thyratron from firing. When an object approaches the sensing plate, the grid of V1 becomes more positive. At the same instant, the grid of V2 becomes more positive, and V2 fires, thus activating the relay. When the object is removed from vicinity of the sensing plate, the negative grid voltage of V2 is restored, the tube ceases firing, and relay K1 opens. You may be wondering how restoring the negative grid bias of the thyratron (V2) will cause it to cease firing. We said earlier that once a thyratron fired, its control grid lost all control. Because V2 is operated from an a-c plate voltage supply the control of V2 is restored to its control grid. The plate of V2 swings negative with respect to its cathode on every negative alternation of the applied a-c plate voltage. This is the same as turning its plate voltage off for every negative alternation. When its plate again becomes positive with respect to its cathode, the gas in the tube is not ionized and the control grid can again take control of thyratron V2.

Construction

As in the previous units, this proximity detector is not particularly critical with respect to either mechanical or component layout. The component substitutions indicated in the oscillator section of the two-stage proximity detector (Fig. 2-4) apply to this circuit also. A 5727 (7-pin miniature) or 2050 (octal) tube may be substituted for the 2D21 indicated on the schematic. It will be necessary to substitute an octal socket for the 7 pin miniature socket used for the 2D21 when using the 2050 tube. Fig. 2-10 is the pictorial diagram for this circuit.

Operation

With a sensing plate (4″ × 4″ metal plate), or length of wire connected to the grid of V1, apply a-c power to the chassis. After waiting about 30 seconds for the tubes to reach operating temperature, increase the capacitance of C1 until the relay de-energizes. Decrease the capacitance of C1 until the relay energizes, then increase its capacitance until the relay just opens.

Because of the excellent sensitivity of this detector, you will find a wide number of applications for it, and the operating range can be extended a foot or more by a larger sensor.

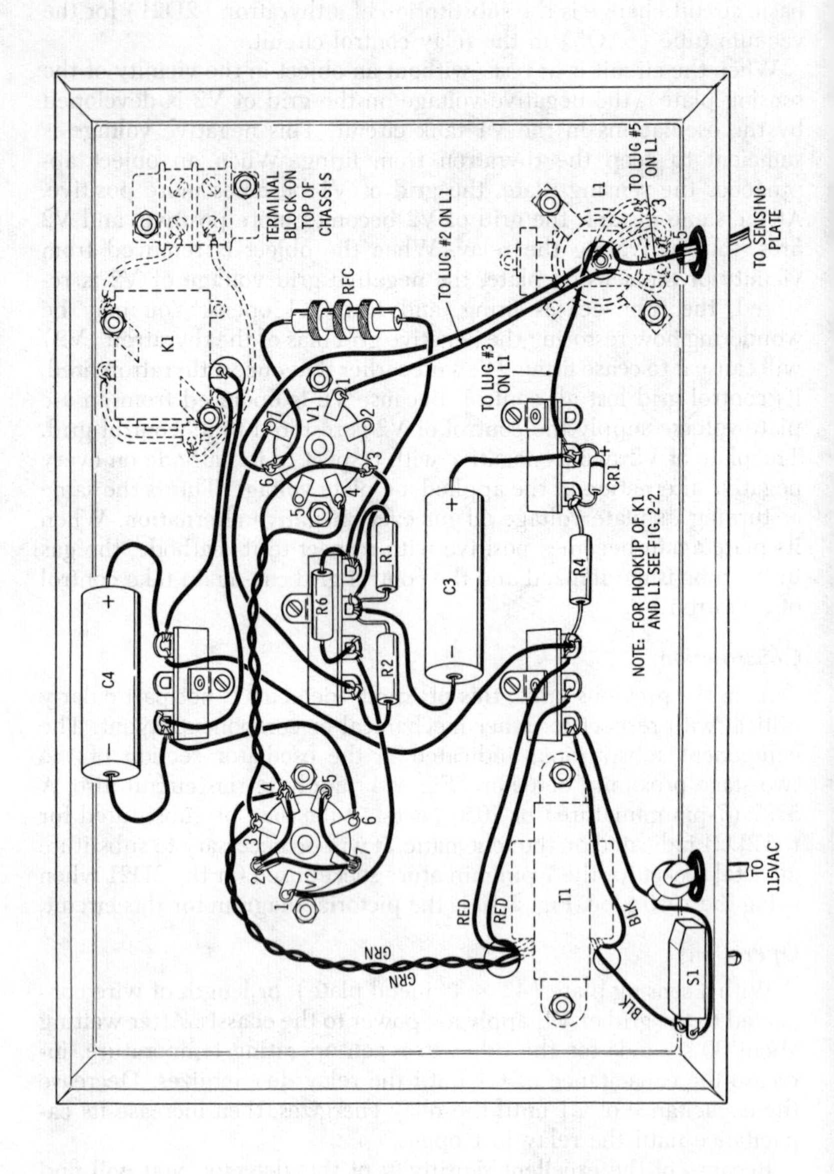

Fig. 2-10. Pictorial diagram for Fig. 2-9.

Addition of Latch Function

The two-stage proximity detector with latching relay (Fig. 2-7) required a dpdt relay in its design. A separate set of contacts was required to properly switch its relay coil to the latching mode. Since the proximity detector in Fig. 2-9 uses a thyratron as the relay control tube, we can take advantage of its "self-latching" characteristics and use a simpler spdt relay.

As shown in Fig. 2-11, the thyratron is operated with a d-c rather than a-c plate voltage, and a reset switch is placed in series with its plate-supply return lead. The pictorial diagram in Fig. 2-12 shows this circuit with the incorporated latch function.

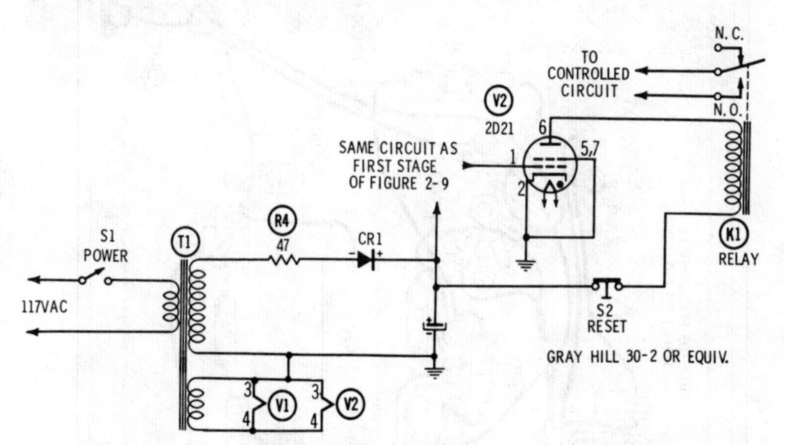

Fig. 2-11. Adding latching action to Fig. 2-9 circuit.

When the grid voltage of V2 becomes more positive due to a drop in the negative grid voltage of V1 (as a result of an object approaching the sensing plate), V2 fires, thus energizing relay K1. Since V2 is operated with a d-c plate voltage, once it fires, V2 will continue to fire even after its control grid again goes negative (when the object leaves the vicinity of the sensing plate). To reset the unit, the reset switch is pushed to remove plate voltage from V2. V2 de-ionizes and relay K1 opens.

Addition of Ratchet Relay

There is a need for a proximity detector which will switch a device on and remain on until the sensor is again touched. Applications for this type of operation include lamps, appliances, etc. which are intended to stay on until turned off by the second action of a relay switch.

To adapt the preceding proximity detector with thyratron relay control (Fig. 2-9) for this type of operation, it is only necessary to

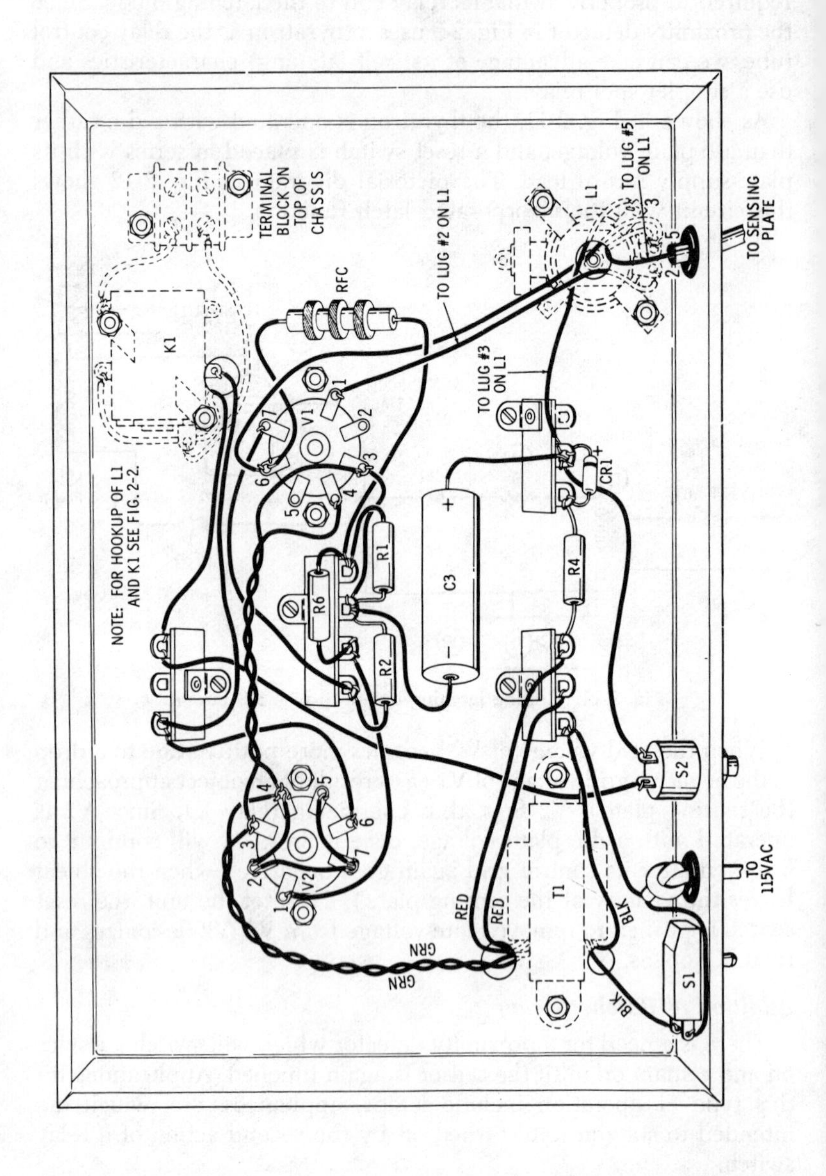

Fig. 2-12. Pictorial diagram for Fig. 2-11.

obtain a ratchet relay K3, sometimes referred to as an impulse relay, and connect it as shown in Fig. 2-13. A satisfactory impulse relay for this purpose is the Potter-Brumfield Type AP1-1A or equivalent which is available at most major electronic parts distributors. Fig. 2-14 is the pictorial diagram of this circuit.

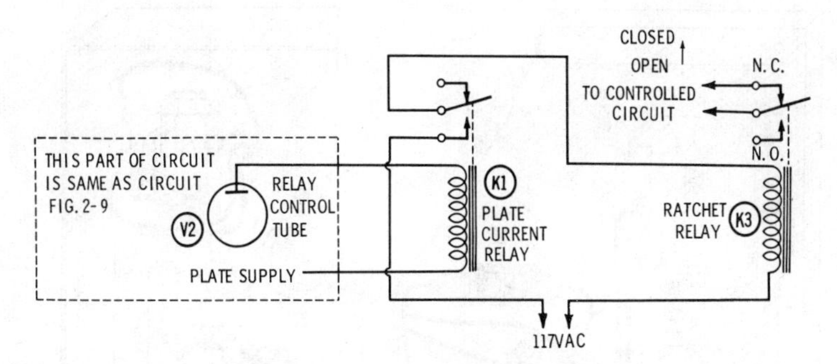

Fig. 2-13. A two-stage, loaded-oscillator proximity detector with thyratron controlled ratchet relay.

Each time the 117V a-c current is applied to the coil of K3 by the contacts of plate-circuit relay K1, the driving ratchet of impulse relay K3 advances one notch. The contacts of K3 alternately switch from normally open to normally closed position and vice-versa. Any device connected in series with contacts of K3 will be alternately turned on and off each time the sensor is approached.

SINGLE-STAGE A-C FIELD-EXCITED TOUCHSWITCH

So far, we have been talking about proximity detection by means of a loaded oscillator. In the loaded oscillator, a built-in oscillator stage provides the signal to generate the control voltage. A different approach for generation of the oscillator signal is the use of 60-cycle field generated by an a-c power line. The a-c power lines radiate strong electromagnetic and electrostatic fields. These fields produce a loud hum when you touch the input of an audio amplifier. It is possible to use these same a-c fields in the development of several proximity detectors.

Circuit Description

Fig. 2-15 is the simplest of these circuits, consisting of thyratron V1; relay K1; potentiometer R8; fixed resistors R1, R4, and R5; filter capacitor C4; isolation/power transformer T1; spst switch S1; push-button switch S2; and silicon diode CR1. The small amount of components required for this circuit is shown in Fig. 2-16.

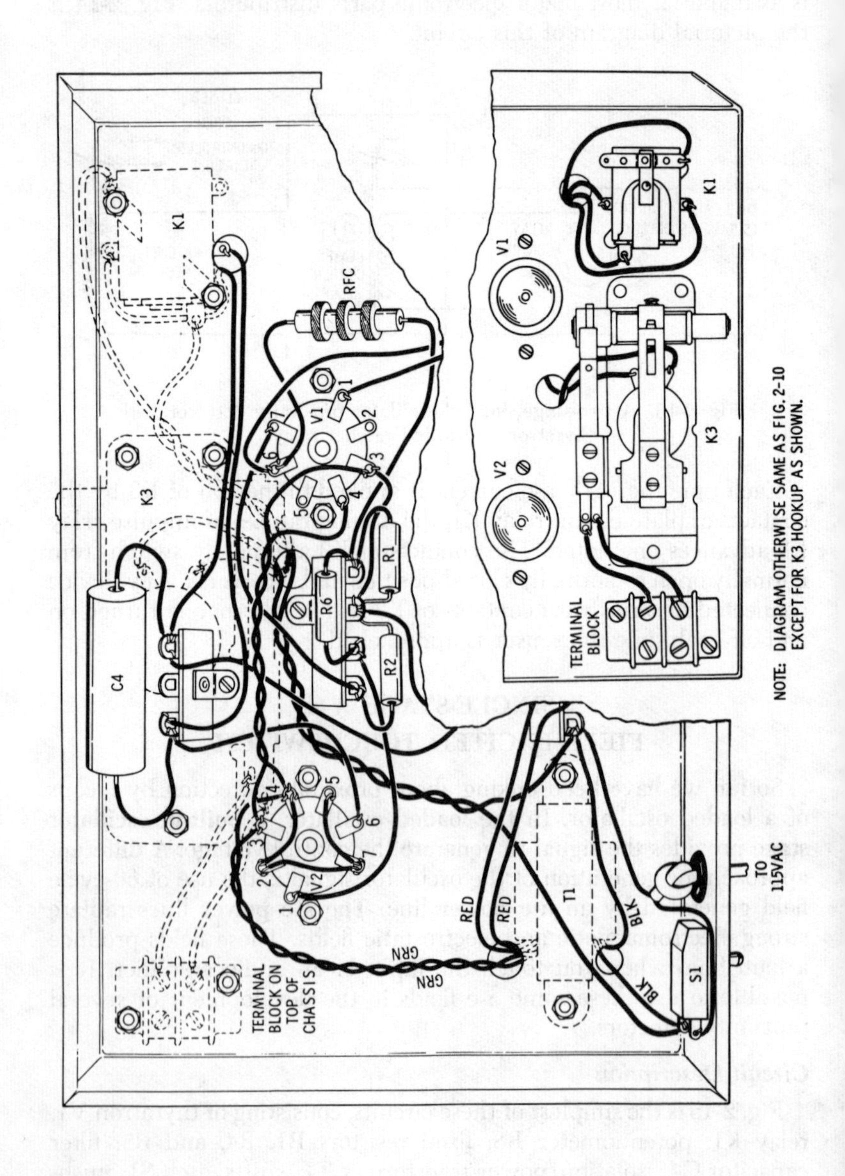

Fig. 2-14. Pictorial diagram for Fig. 2-13.

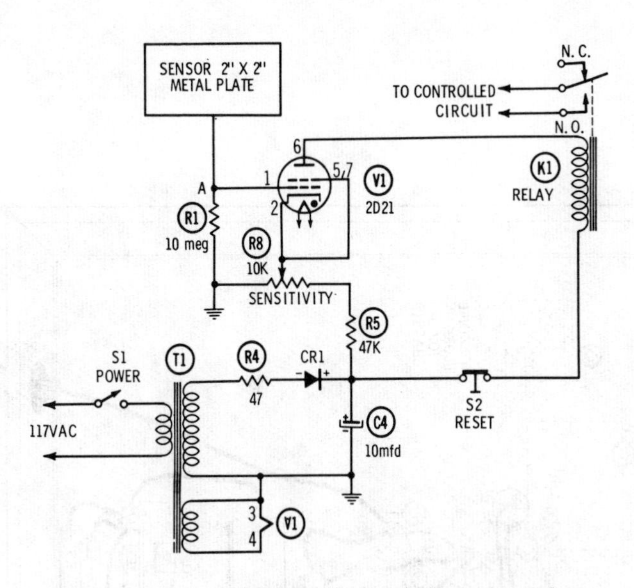

Fig. 2-15. A single-stage, field-excited touchswitch.

Parts List for Fig. 2-15

Item	Description
C4	Capacitor, 10 mfd, 150v, electrolytic
CR1	Rectifier, silicon, 1N2484 or equiv.
K1	Relay, 5000 ohm d-c coil, spdt contacts, Potter Brumfield RS5D or equiv.
R1	Resistor,10 megohm, ½ watt
R4	Resistor, 47 ohm, ½ watt
R5	Resistor, 47K ohm, ½ watt
R8	Potentiometer, 10K ohm, 2 watt
S1	Switch, toggle, spst
S2	Switch, push button, n.c., spst, Grayhill 30-2 or equiv.
T1	Transformer, power, pri. 117v, sec. 125v @ 50 ma, sec. 6.3v @ 2 amp
V1	Tube, 2D21

The circuit operates as follows: Thyratron V1 is supplied with d-c plate voltage from the power supply, which consists of T1, CR1, R4, and C4. Relay K1 is connected in the plate circuit of V1 so that it will be actuated when V1 fires. The sensitivity control (R8) is adjusted without an object near the sensor until the cathode of V1 is slightly more positive than its control grid. This is the same as making the control grid of V1 negative with respect to its cathode.

When an object touches the sensor, a portion of the a-c field radiated from the power lines is introduced into the control grid

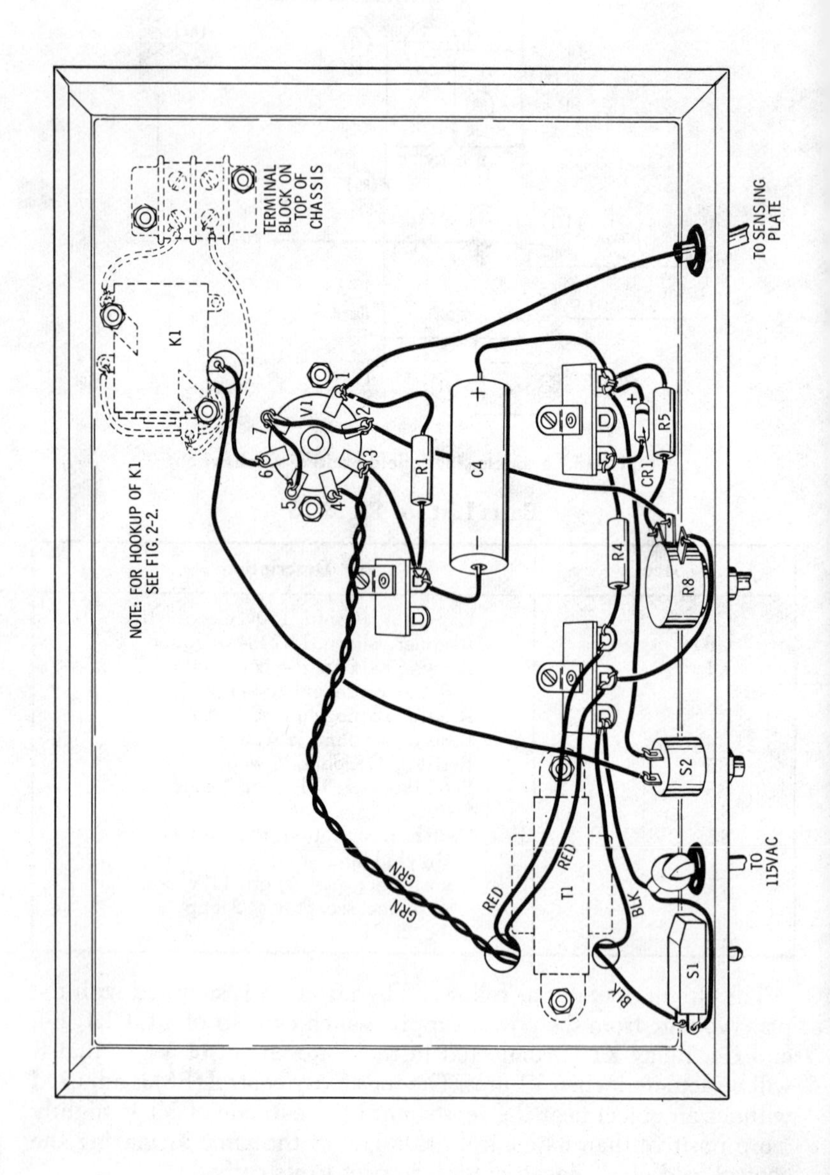

Fig. 2-16. Pictorial diagram for Fig. 2-15.

circuit of V1. This 60-cycle signal is sufficient to fire V1, which energizes relay K1. Once triggered, V1 will continue to fire until the reset switch (S2) is pushed to break the plate circuit.

Construction

This unit is assembled on a small chassis. The placement of the electronic parts is not critical, and you can use any size chassis. Electronic components may be substituted as follows: V1 may be replaced with a 5727 (7 pin miniature) or 2050 (octal) tube. The tube socket will have to be changed for the octal tube. R1 can be between 10 and 20 megohms and C1 between 10 and 40 mfd. The relay may have a coil resistance ranging from 2.5K to 10K ohms. A selenium rectifier may be substituted for silicon diode CR1.

Adjustment

Attach a sensing plate (about 2″ × 2″ metal) to the control grid of V1. Apply power to the circuit. When V1 has reached operating temperature, adjust sensitivity control R2 until relay K1 is de-energized. The thyratron will fire when the sensor is touched and energize the relay. The relay will now remain energized until the reset switch is pushed to open the plate circuit.

If too large a sensor is used with this circuit, relay K1 will not open with any setting of R8 because of the excessive a-c field picked up by sensor. This signal on the control grid of V1 overrides the bias established by R8, regardless of how close the object is to the sensor.

SINGLE-STAGE TOUCHSWITCH WITH 60-CYCLE FIELD EXCITATION AND NEON-CONTROLLED RELAY

This proximity detector is an unusual device. It does not consume power until it is actuated. The circuit is designed around an NE-77 (three electrode) neon tube. Current is consumed by this circuit only when a voltage is developed across grid-cathode of V1. This occurs when an object approaches the proximity-detector sensor and triggers neon lamp V1.

Because of the simplicity and cool operation (no power consumption until actuated) of this device, it can be assembled into a compact package. It is economical to build, maintain, and operate.

Circuit Description

The schematic is shown in Fig. 2-17. The heart of the unit is V1 (NE-77), which is similar to an NE-2 neon lamp, except that the NE-77 contains a third electrode centrally located between the two outer electrodes. As long as the voltage applied to the center electrode of V1 is held below a ionization level, it will not fire. When the voltage applied to the center electrode becomes more positive than the ionization level, V1 will suddenly fire, and current will flow between its two outer electrodes.

As shown in Fig. 2-17, d-c voltage is applied to one outer electrode of V1 from the power supply. The other electrode is connected to one terminal of relay coil K1. The opposite relay coil terminal is returned to the power line via the normally closed reset switch.

A voltage divider, consisting of R1, R2, and R3 is connected across the power supply. The slider of sensitivity control R1 is adjusted (without an object near the sensor) until the voltage applied to the center electrode of V1 will not be sufficient to cause the neon lamp to fire.

When an object touches the sensor, an a-c voltage will be applied to the center electrode of V1; V1 will fire and energize the relay K1. The relay will then remain energized until the reset switch is pushed to open the circuit.

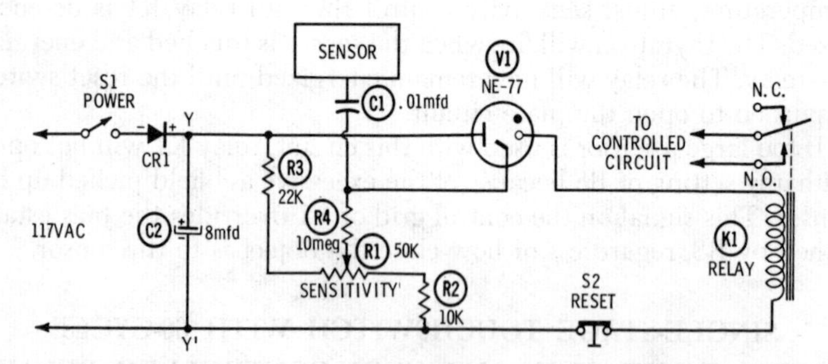

Fig. 2-17. A single-stage touchswitch with 60-cycle excitation and neon-controlled relay.

Parts List for Fig. 2-17

Item	Description
C1	Capacitor, .01 mfd, 200v, paper
C2	Capacitor, 8 mfd, 150v, electrolytic
CR1	Rectifier, silicon, 1N2484 or equiv.
K1	Relay, 5000 ohm d-c coil, spdt contacts, Potter Brumfield RS5D or equiv.
R1	Potentiometer, 50K ohm, 1 watt, wirewound
R2	Resistor, 10K ohm, ½ watt
R3	Resistor, 22K ohm, ½ watt
S1	Switch, toggle, spst
S2	Switch, push button, normally closed, Grayhill 30-2 or equiv.
V1	Lamp, NE77, neon

Construction

The touchswitch is assembled on a small piece of perforated phenolic board. Point-to-point wiring was used with connections being made to small terminal lugs inserted through the holes in the board. Fig. 2-18 is the pictorial diagram for this circuit.

Placement of electronic parts is not critical. You can use your own imagination in layout and packaging of the complete unit. Electronic components can be substituted as follows: C1 may be any value from 0.01 to .1 mfd, C2 may range from 8 to 40 mfd, and CR1 may be either a silicon or selenium rectifier.

Adjustment

Adjustment of the unit is simple. Apply power and adjust the sensitivity potentiometer (without an object near the sensor) until the relay is de-energized. Now touch the sensor—the relay should energize and stay energized until the reset switch is pushed to open the circuit. The relay will remain energized for all settings of R1 when the sensing plate is too large.

This detector can be easily made into a portable unit by replacing the a-c line power with batteries. Connect two, series-connected, 67½-volt batteries to points Y and Y′ on Fig. 2-17. Filter capacitor C2 can be eliminated when operating the unit from batteries.

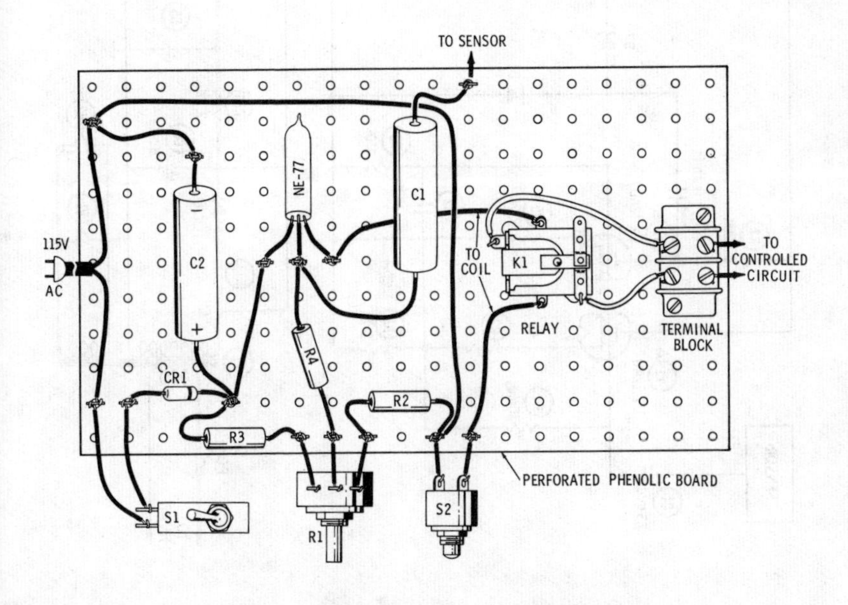

Fig. 2-18. Pictorial diagram for Fig. 2-17.

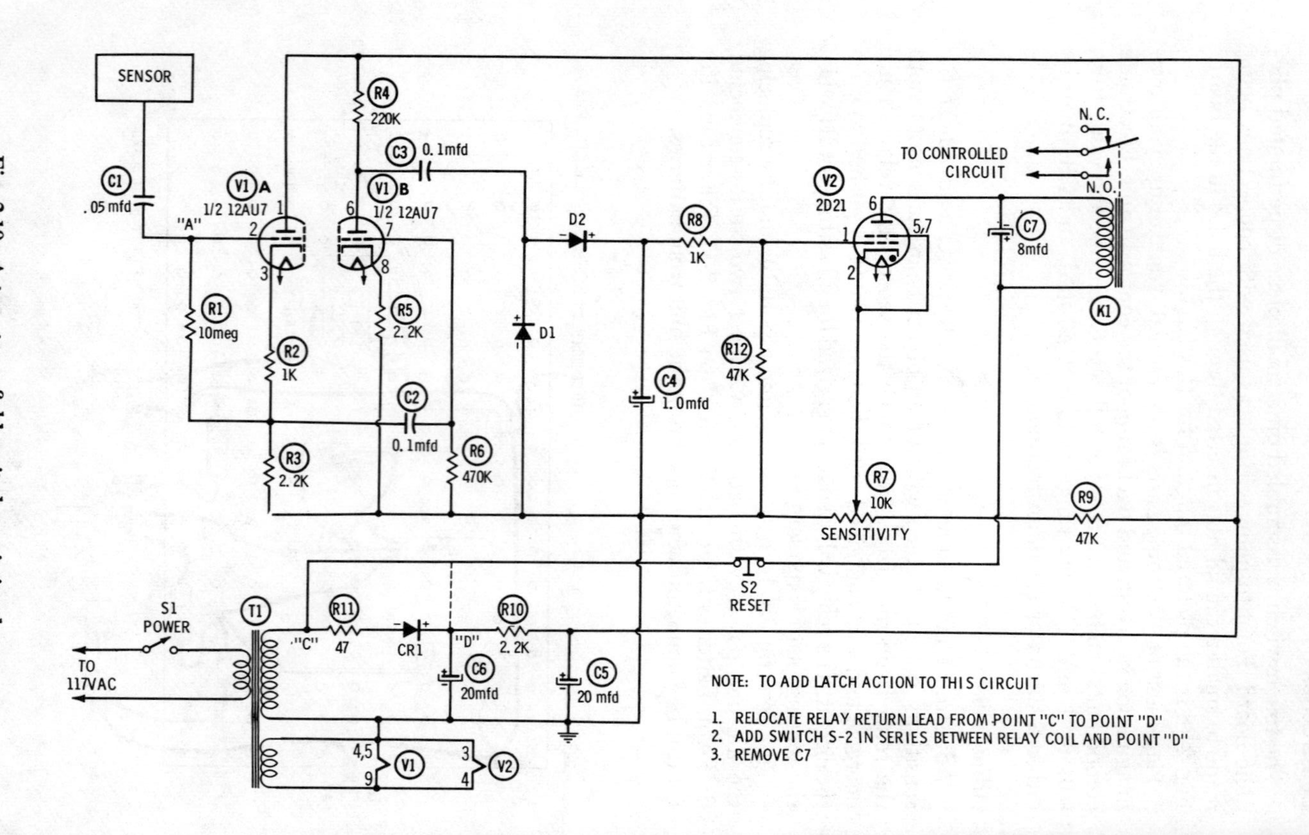

Fig. 2-19. A two-stage, field-excited proximity detector.

Parts List for Fig. 2-19

Item	Description
C1	Capacitor, .05 mfd, 200v, paper
C2, C3	Capacitors, 0.1 mfd, 200v, paper
C4	Capacitor, 1.0 mfd, 200v, paper
C5, C6	Capacitors, 20 mfd, 150v, electrolytic
C7	Capacitor, 8 mfd, 150v, electrolytic
CR1	Rectifier, silicon, 1N2484 or equiv.
D1, D2	Diodes, 1N34A, crystal
K1	Relay, 5000 ohm d-c coil, spdt contacts, Potter Brumfield RS5D or equiv.
R1	Resistor, 10 megohm, ½ watt
R2, R8	Resistors, 1K ohm, ½ watt
R3, R5, R10	Resistors, 2.2K ohm, ½ watt
R4	Resistor, 220K ohm, ½ watt
R6	Resistor, 470K ohm, ½ watt
R7	Potentiometer, 10K, linear, wirewound
R9, R12	Resistors, 47K ohm, ½ watt
S1	Switch, toggle, spst
S2	Switch, push button, n.c., Grayhill 30-2 or equiv.
T1	Transformer, pri. 117 volts, sec. 125v @ 50 ma, 6.3v @ 2 amp
V1	Tube, 12AU7
V2	Tube, thyratron, 2D21

TWO-STAGE FIELD-EXCITED PROXIMITY DETECTOR

The relatively low sensitivity of the two previous a-c field-operated proximity detectors limits them to "touchswitch" operation. For increased sensitivity, the circuit of Fig. 2-19 is recommended. Improved sensitivity is a result of a cathode-follower input stage which exhibits a very high input impedance with low output impedance, making possible a unit that is very responsive to slight changes in the a-c field picked up by the sensor.

Circuit Description

As shown in Fig. 2-19, the circuit consists of a two-stage amplifier feeding a thyratron relay control stage.

Referring to the schematic (Fig. 2-19), when an object approaches the sensor, an a-c signal resulting from radiation of an a-c field by the powerlines is applied to the control grid of V1A. Since V1A is connected as a cathode follower, it presents a high impedance to the input circuit. Therefore the incoming signal voltage will be of considerable amplitude even for a small input signal current.

The signal derived from the sensor is applied via the cathode follower through capacitor C2, and V1B amplifies the signal and applies it to the voltage-doubler rectifier comprised of C3, D1, D2, and C4.

The resulting positive d-c output voltage from the voltage-doubler rectifier will have an amplitude proportional to the amplitude of the signal appearing at the sensor. The d-c signal is applied to the relay control stage consisting of thyratron V2, sensitivity control R7, and relay K1.

Without an object near the sensor, R7 is adjusted so that the cathode of V2 is slightly more positive than its control grid. This bias prevents V2 from firing. When an object approaches the sensing plate, the resulting positive voltage is applied to the control grid of V2. This causes the grid of V2 to become more positive than the cathode, and the tube will fire, energizing the relay. Since V2 is supplied with an a-c plate voltage, it will cease firing when the positive voltage is removed from its control grid—when the object is moved away from sensor. The capacitor connected across the relay coil prevents the relay from chattering when the thyratron is operated.

The power supply is a conventional circuit, consisting of power/isolation transformer T1, silicon diode CR1, filter capacitors C5 and C6, filter resistors R10 and R11, and power switch S1.

Construction

This unit can be assembled on a small chassis. Component layout is not critical. Short leads are used in the first stage—particularly between the grid of V1A and the sensor terminal. Also, all filament leads must be routed as far away as possible from the grid and plate leads of V1A and V1B to minimize the induction of 60-cycle signals into these circuits. Fig. 2-20 shows routing of wiring.

Components can be substituted as follows: R2 may range from 1K to 2.7K, R3 (10K to 22K), R4 (150K to 220K, R6 (470K to 1 meg), C2 (0.1 to 1.0 mfd), and R10 (1K to 2.2K).

Adjustment

Check the wiring hookup with the schematic (Fig. 2-19), and then connect the sensor to terminal A. Apply a-c power to the circuit. With no object near the sensor, adjust the sensitivity control (R7) until thyratron V2 does not fire. Your hand placed near the sensor should cause the thyratron to fire and energize the relay. Remove your hand, and the relay will de-energize. The thyratron will fire for all settings of R7 if the size of the sensor is too large.

Addition of Latch Function

To convert the proximity relay in Fig. 2-19 to latching relay action, make the changes indicated by dashed lines in Fig. 2-19, and remove

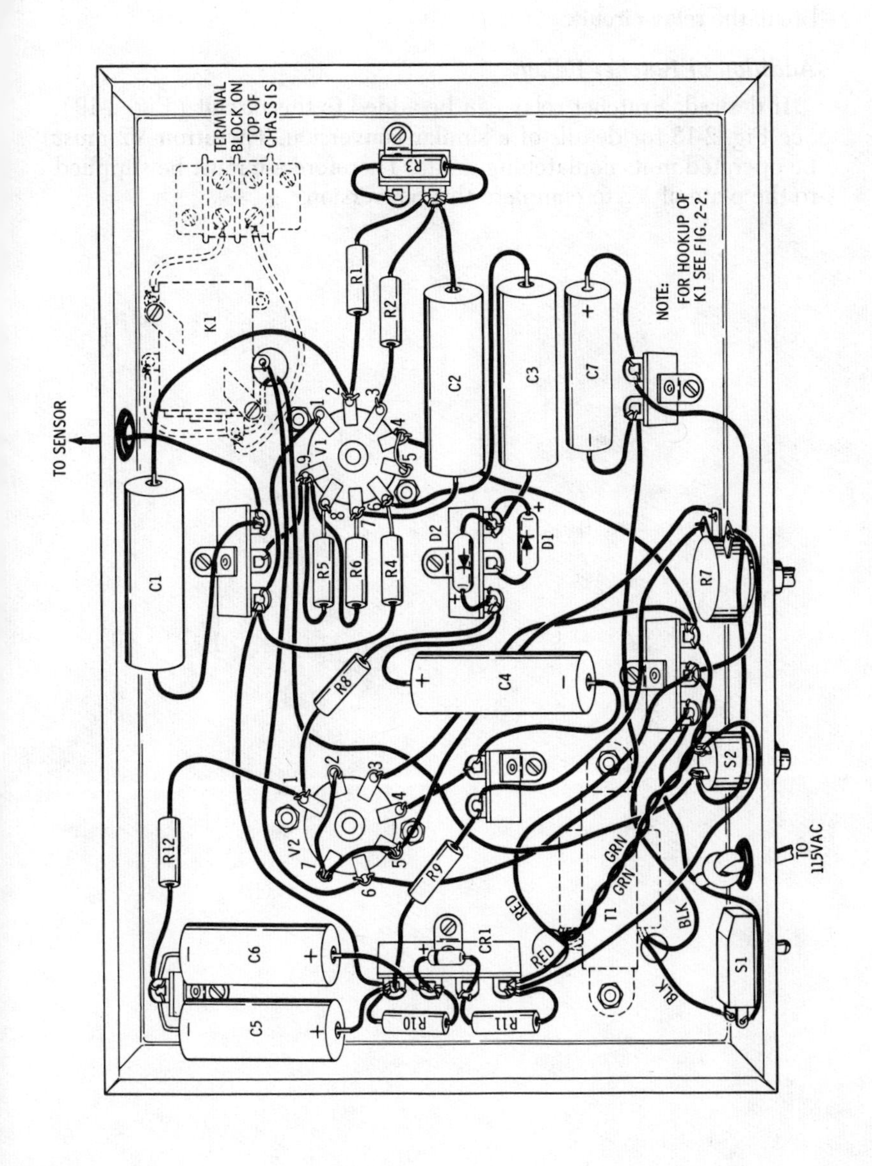

Fig. 2-20. Pictorial diagram for Fig. 2-19.

C7. The plate of V2 is now supplied with a d-c voltage. When an object approaches the sensor, the d-c voltage developed by the voltage doubler (D1, D2, C3, C4) is applied to the control grid of V2. V2 fires and remains in this mode until reset switch S2 is pushed to break the relay circuit.

Addition of Ratchet Relay

If desired, a ratchet relay can be added to this circuit (Fig. 2-19). See Fig. 2-13 for details of a similar conversion. Thyratron V2 must be operated in its nonlatching mode. Therefore a-c must be supplied to the plate of V2 to complete this conversion.

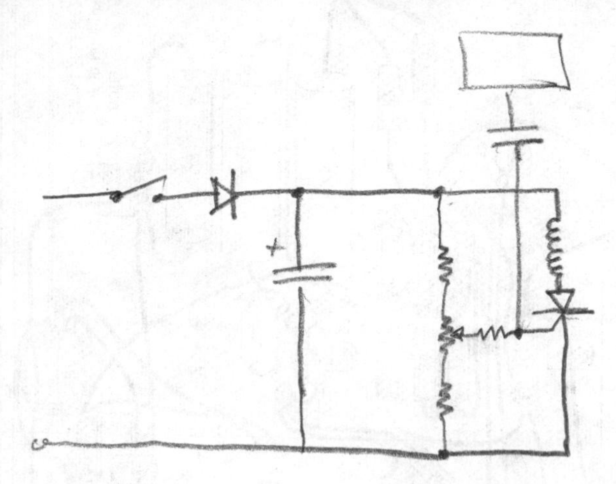

Chapter 3

Advanced Proximity Detectors

Since we have completed some relatively simple proximity detectors, we are ready to undertake the construction of the more sophisticated circuits. The proximity detectors described in this chapter have a number of special features which make them adaptable to a wide variety of applications. In fact, the unusual features of a number of the units to be described should make them attractive as Science Fair projects.

FOUR-STAGE BEAT-FREQUENCY PROXIMITY DETECTOR

The necessity for the location of the oscillator close to sensor (to secure short oscillator circuit wiring) is a major problem with the "loaded-oscillator" principle of proximity detection. Any attempt to locate the sensor at a point remote from the oscillator will result in a number of problems. For example, the shunt capacitance of a shielded input cable will drastically reduce the sensitivity of the proximity detector. If the input cable is not shielded, the lead will act as a sensor, and it must be kept clear of all nearby objects.

Circuit Description

Fig. 3-1 is the schematic of a circuit that will eliminate these problems. With this circuit, the sensor can be located as far as 10 feet from the chassis with no change in the circuit performance.

The basic circuit consists of a fixed and a variable frequency oscillator (vfo). The frequency of the variable oscillator (part of mixer tube V2) will change as a result of a change in the overall shunt capacitance across the variable oscillator tank circuit. This capacitance changes when an object approaches the vicinity of the sensor. This change in the variable oscillator frequency will produce a heterodyne (or beat) frequency with the preset fixed oscillator (V1A)

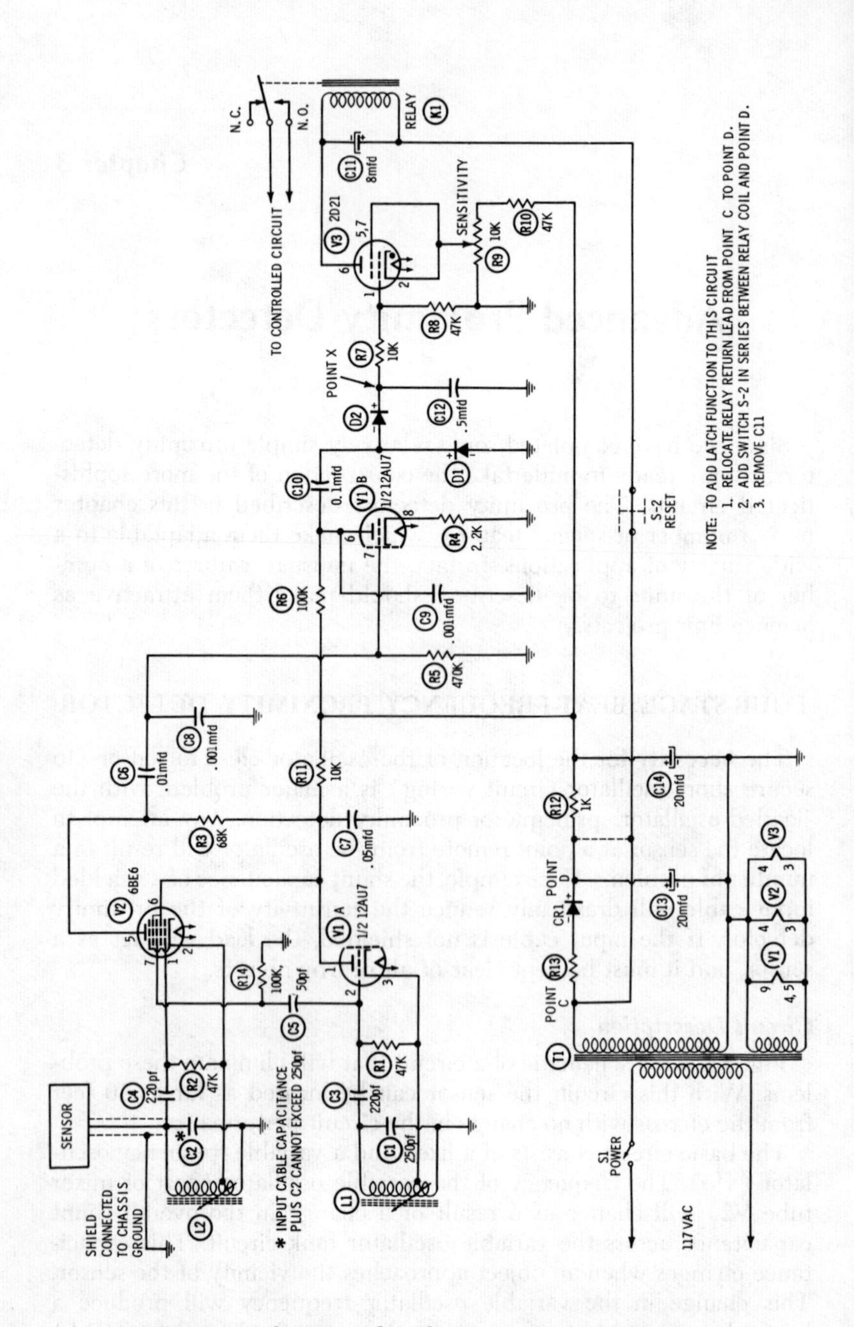

Fig. 3-1. A four-stage, beat-frequency proximity detector.

Parts List for Fig. 3-1

Item	Description
C1	Capacitors, 250 pf, mica
C2	Capacitor, mica (see schematic)
C3, C4	Capacitors, 220 pf, mica
C5	Capacitor, 50 pf, mica
C6	Capacitor, .01 mfd, paper
C7	Capacitor, .05 mfd, paper
C8, C9	Capacitors, .001 mfd, paper
C10	Capacitor, 0.1 mfd, paper
C11	Capacitor, 8 mfd, 150v, electrolytic
C12	Capacitor, 0.5 mfd, paper
C13, C14	Capacitors, 20 mfd, 150v, electrolytic
CR1	Rectifier, silicon, 1N2484 or equiv.
D1, D2	Diodes, 1N34A, crystal
K1	Relay, 5000 ohm d-c coil, spdt contacts, Potter Brumfield RS5D or equiv.
L1, L2	Coils, antenna, ferrite core, J. W. Miller no. 9012 or equiv.
R1, R2, R8, R10	Resistors, 47K, ½ watt
R3	Resistor, 68K, ½ watt
R4	Resistor, 2.2K, ½ watt
R5	Resistor, 470K, ½ watt
R6, R14	Resistor, 100K, ½ watt
R7, R11	Resistors, 10K, ½ watt
R9	Resistor, 10K, 1 watt
R12	Resistor, 1K, 1 watt
R13	Resistor, 47, ½ watt
S1	Switch, toggle, spst
S2	Switch, push button, normally closed, spst, Grayhill 30-2 or equiv.
T1	Transformer, pri. 117v, sec. 125v @ 50 ma, 6.3 v @ 2 amp
V1	Tube, 12AU7
V2	Tube, 6BE6, converter
V3	Tube, 2D21, thyratron

frequency in the mixer stage (V2). The beat frequency is determined by the change in the frequency of the variable oscillator.

The beat frequency is applied to a filter (C8 and C9) which provides an output voltage that varies in proportion to the applied frequency. This output voltage will increase as the frequency is decreased. After amplification by V1B, the signal is rectified by a voltage doubler (C10, D1, D2, and C12) and applied to the control grid of thyratron V3. V3 fires and energizes relay K1.

Now we will examine this circuit more closely. The two oscillator circuits form the heart of the circuit. The fixed-frequency oscillator, consisting of V1A, L1, C1, C3, and R1, is a standard Hartley oscillator using a loopstick (ferrite core antenna-coil) as the oscillator coil. The fixed oscillator with the values shown in Fig. 3-1 can be adjusted between 500 to 800 kc by L1. The vfo consists of L2, C2, C4, R2, and V2. The component values except C2 for this oscillator are identical to those for the fixed oscillator.

To obtain the desired heterodyning action, a portion of the r-f signal developed by the fixed-frequency oscillator is applied to grid No. 3 (Pin 7) of V2 via C5. The r-f signals generated by the two oscillators will heterodyne in V2, and the resulting beat frequency will appear at the plate of V2. This signal consists of the desired beat-frequency signal which is the difference between the two oscillator frequencies, plus a signal which is the sum of the two oscillator frequencies. For example, if the fixed-frequency oscillator is operating at 500 kc and the variable-frequency oscillator at 510 kc, the difference frequency will be 510 kc minus 500 kc or 10 kc. The sum of these two oscillator frequencies will be 500 kc plus 510 kc or 1010 kc.

The difference, or intermediate, frequency signal, stripped of the sum signal by low-pass filter C8 and C9 is coupled to the i-f amplifier stage consisting of V1B, R4, R5, R6, and C8. The purpose of this stage is to amplify the i-f signal before it is applied to the rectifier.

Capacitors C8 and C9 serve as simple low-pass filters to give the circuit the desired output voltage versus frequency characteristics. To see just what we mean by this statement, look at Fig. 3-2, which shows an approximation of the output voltage appearing at the plate of V1B for various i-f frequencies. Notice that as the i-f frequency increases, the signal output voltage will decrease.

Now we will take a look at the overall circuit up to the grid of V3. The fixed-frequency and variable-frequency oscillators are adjusted

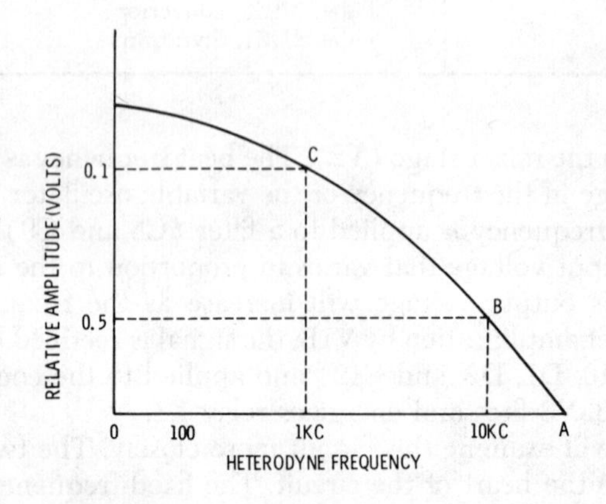

Fig. 3-2. Filter characteristics.

without an object near the sensing plate for a difference frequency greater than 10 kc—point A in Fig. 3-2. According to the curve in Fig. 3-2, this i-f signal will produce a signal output voltage of zero volts at the plate of V1B. We will now move the object closer to the sensor, and the capacitance between the object and sensor will increase. Since the sensing plate shunts tank circuit L2-C2 of the variable frequency oscillator, this will change the frequency of the oscillator. With proper adjustment of the vfo, this increase in the shunt capacitance across L2-C3 will result in a lower i-f frequency. This reduced frequency will cause a greater output signal to be developed at the filters (C8-C9) so that a larger signal will appear at the plate of V1B (points B and C in Fig. 3-2).

The signal appearing at the plate of V1B is applied to a voltage doubler and rectifier (D1, D2, C10 and C12) and a positive output voltage is developed. This voltage is applied to the control grid of thyratron-relay control tube V3. Without an object near the sensor, the sensitivity control (R9) is adjusted so that the cathode of V3 is slightly more positive than the control grid. Under these conditions, V3 will not fire, and the relay will not be energized.

When an object approaches the sensor, the positive output voltage from the voltage doubler and rectifier increases, and the grid of V3 becomes more positive than its cathode. This will cause V3 to fire and energize the relay. Since V3 is operated with an a-c plate-voltage supply, it will cease to fire when the output of the voltage doubler and rectifier decreases to zero. The output voltage of this rectifier is zero when no object is near the sensor.

Earlier in this chapter we mentioned that this three-stage proximity detector circuit could be used with a remotely located sensor. As shown in Fig. 3-1, the sensor is connected to the vfo by means of a shielded cable. This feature is made possible because the capacitance of the shielded cable forms an integral part of the vfo and can be "cancelled out" by an equal amount of "balancing capacitance" in the fixed-frequency oscillator. For example, if the total capacitance of a 5-foot length of coaxial cable (used to connect the sensor to the variable-frequency oscillator) is 100 pf, and the value of fixed tank circuit capacitance is 250 pf, the total capacitance of the tank circuit of variable-frequency oscillator must also total 250 picofarads. The total capacitance of each oscillator (fixed and variable) must be equal to the total capacitance of the other oscillator to obtain approximately the same frequency from both oscillators. As a practical example, assume we want to have a 5-foot separation between the sensor and the tank circuit of a variable oscillator. A typical cable should be RG59B/U, which has a capacitance of 20.5 pf per foot, or a total of 102.5 pf for the 5 feet of cable. If the total capacitance of fixed-frequency oscillator tank circuit capacitance has been adjusted by C2 to 250 pf, capacitor C1 of the vfo must be 147.5 picofarads. The total capacitance of the vfo-tank circuit will now be 147.5 pf plus the 102.5 pf of the lead-in cable capacitance, or 250 picofarads.

Construction

The beat-frequency proximity detector is assembled on a small chassis. Although short and direct leads should be used in the two oscillators, the placement of parts is not critical. Also, it is important that the components for the two oscillators be mounted as rigidly as possible to assure maximum stability. To avoid any interaction between the components L1 and L2 should be well separated from each other. This is particularly true in the case of L1 and L2; if they are too close to each other, the two oscillators will tend to lock together (operate on the same frequency), and this tends to reduce the sensitivity. Fig. 3-3 is the pictorial diagram of this circuit.

Components can be substituted as follows: R1 and R2 (22K to 100K), R3 (47K to 100K), R4 (1K to 3.3K), R5 (470K to 1 meg), R6 (100K to 220K), C2 (100 pf to 500 pf), C4 (100 pf to 500 pf), C6 (.01 mfd to a .05 mfd), C10 (0.1 to 0.5 mfd), and C11 (8 mfd to 20 mfd). V1 can be either a 12AU7, 12AT7, or 6SN7; and V4 a 5727 or 2050. The tube sockets must be changed when an octal tube is used instead of a miniature tube.

As shown in the schematic (Fig. 3-1), the coaxial cable is connected between the sensor and the variable-frequency oscillator. The total value of capacitance of the vfo must be within a few picofarad of the total capacitance of the fixed-frequency oscillator. Fig. 3-1 indicates a value of 250 pf across the tank coil L1 or L2 of each oscillator. Therefore, should you wish to change the length of the coaxial cable between the sensing plate and the variable-frequency oscillator, remember that the total capacitance of cable *and* the variable oscillator must be 250 picofarad.

Adjustment

The sensor with attached lead-in cable is connected to the proximity detector chassis and 115 a-c power is applied to the chassis. Temporarily connect a jumper from point X to chassis ground (Fig. 3-1), and adjust the sensitivity control (R9) until V3 does not fire. Remove the jumper, and turn the slugs of L1 and L2 half way into the coils. Without an object near the sensor, increase the inductance of L2 by turning the slug clockwise into the coil, until thyratron V4 fires, and the relay energizes. Now, turn the slug counterclockwise until the relay just de-energizes. Bringing your hand near the sensing plate should energize the relay. If it does not, you are on the "wrong side" of the heterodyne signal. Readjust the variable-oscillator tank slug as follows: without an object near the sensor, turn the slug of

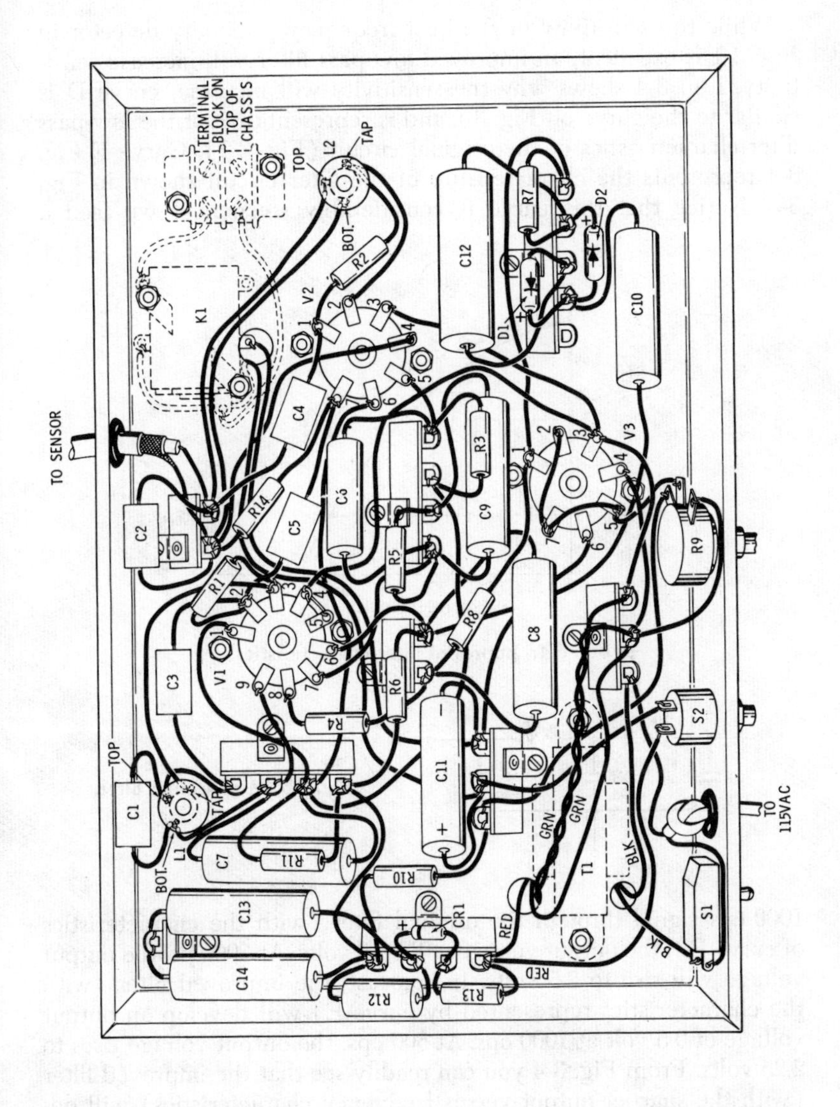

Fig. 3-3. Pictorial diagram for Fig. 3-1.

L2 clockwise until the relay energizes, and then keep turning it in the same direction until the relay de-energizes. Bringing your hand near the sensor will now energize the relay.

Improving Sensitivity

While the sensitivity of the beat-frequency proximity detector in Fig. 3-1 is excellent, an improved low-pass filter will increase sensitivity. Fig. 3-4 shows why the sensitivity will increase; curve D is similar to the curve on Fig. 3-2 and is representative of the low-pass filter characteristics of the original circuit (Fig. 3-1). Curve E Fig. 3-4 represents the characteristics of the filter circuit shown in Fig. 3-5. Notice that this curve is considerably steeper. If we feed a

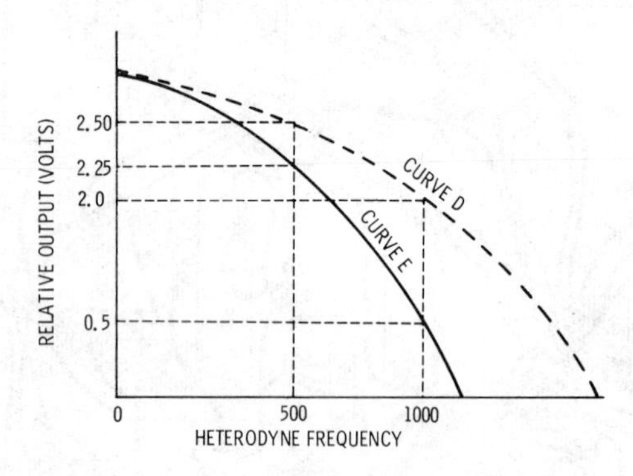

Fig. 3-4. Improved filter characteristics.

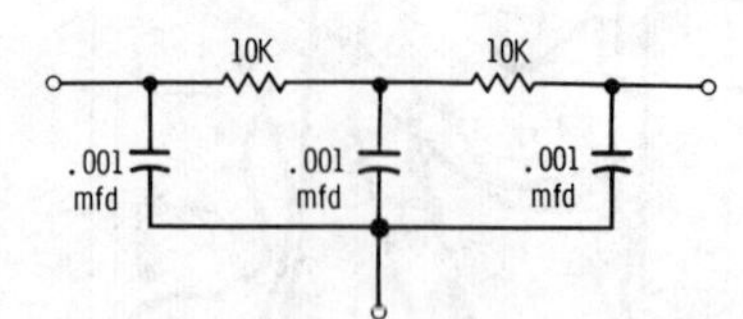

Fig. 3-5. A pi-section filter.

1000-cps signal through the original filter (with the characteristics of curve D), the output voltage will be 2 volts. At 500 cps, the output voltage will rise to 2.5 volts. In contrast, the improved filter (with the characteristics represented by curve E) will develop an output voltage of 0.5 volt at 1000 cps. At 500 cps, the output voltage rises to 2.25 volts. From Fig. 3-4 you can readily see that the improved filter (with the sharper output versus frequency characteristics) will develop a greater output-voltage change for the same frequency change. Since an increase in capacitance between the sensor and the approaching object will develop a given change in the resulting beat frequency, the filter with the sharper characteristics will produce a greater change in the output voltage.

The filter shown in Fig. 3-5 is a simple R-C pi-section type which has considerably sharper response than the simple bypass capacitor arrangement used in the original circuit (Fig. 3-1). The simplified schematic of Fig. 3-6 shows where to connect the new filter into the circuit of Fig. 3-1. Adjustment of this proximity detector is the same as the original three-stage detector (Fig. 3-1).

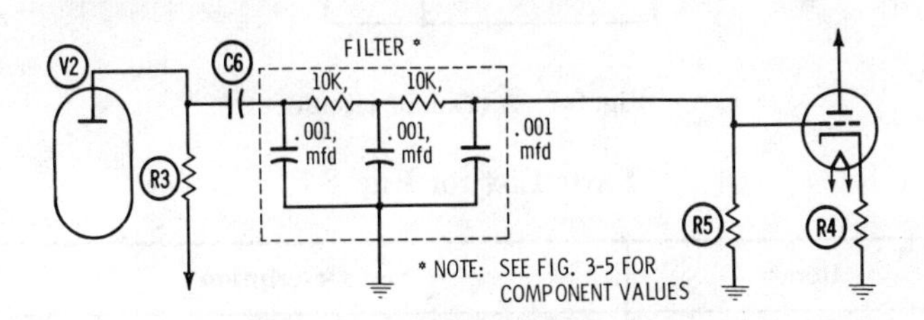

Fig. 3-6. Connection of the pi-section filter into the circuit of Fig. 3-1.

Adding Latch Relay

If you wish, you can add the latching-relay function to the beat-frequency proximity detector (Figs. 3-1 or 3-6). As in the previous proximity detectors using thyratrons, it is necessary to supply thyratron V3 with a source of d-c plate voltage. Also, it is necessary to remove capacitor C11, add a reset switch, and relocate the relay-coil return lead from point C to point D.

THREE-STAGE BEAT-FREQUENCY PROXIMITY DETECTOR WITH METER

In addition to its obvious use as a proximity switch, the beat-frequency proximity detector may be used for a number of other interesting applications. For example, by adding an indicating meter, it can be used as a thickness gauge, vibration sensor, dryness indicator, pressure indicator, liquid-level indicator, and many other applications.

The addition of a meter to the beat-frequency proximity detector is a simple matter if you have a vtvm (vacuum-tube voltmeter) on hand—a vom (volt-ohm-milliammeter) would overload the proximity circuit. If you do not have a vtvm available, the circuit shown in Fig. 3-7 is a satisfactory substitute. It is a basic vtvm circuit, stripped of all unnecessary features, such as the a-c measurement rectifier, and uses only a simple potentiometer at the input instead of the more elaborate voltage divider and range-selector switch. The pictorial diagram for this circuit is shown in Fig. 3-8.

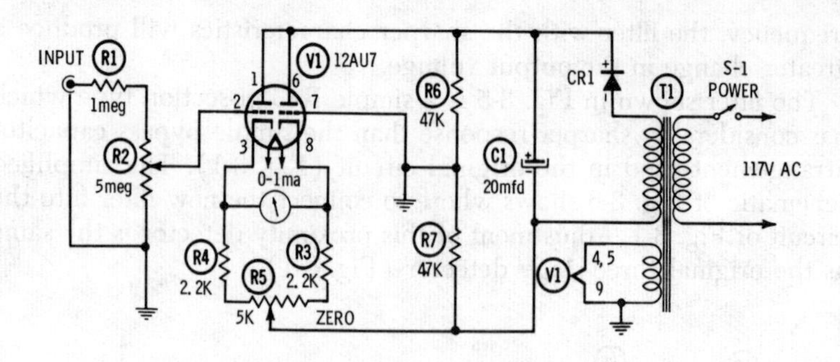

Fig. 3-7. A readout circuit.

Parts List for Fig. 3-7

Item	Description
C1	Capacitor, 20 mfd, 150v, electrolytic
CR1	Rectifier, silicon, 1N2484 or equiv.
M1	Meter, 0-1 ma
R1	Resistor, 1 meg, ½ watt
R2	Potentiometer, 5 meg, 1 watt, linear taper
R3, R4	Resistors, 2.2K, ½ watt
R5	Potentiometer, 5K, 1 watt
R6, R7	Resistors, 47K, ½ watt
S1	Switch, toggle, spst
T1	Transformer, pri. 117v, secondary no. 1 125v @ 50 ma, sec. no. 2 6.3v @ 2 amp
V1	Tube, 12AU7

A ± 10 percent variation in tolerance of the components in the circuit is satisfactory. The meter need not be calibrated in absolute voltage values, since it is used to indicate only relative changes in applied voltage.

The only adjustment required is to zero the meter by means of potentiometer R5 with the input voltage control set to zero (slider at its grounded end).

To use the beat-frequency proximity detector (Fig. 3-1 or 3-6) with a vtvm or the simplified vtvm (Fig. 3-7), connect the positive lead of the vtvm or the input of Fig. 3-7 to pin 1 of V3 and the common lead to ground on proximity detector chassis. It is necessary to remove V3 from the socket when using a meter. Otherwise, the firing of the thyratron will disrupt the meter indication.

With a sensor connected to the proximity detector, a-c line power is applied to the chassis. Without an object near the sensing plate, turn slug L2 clockwise for a maximum indication on the meter. When this point is reached, turn the slug counterclockwise until approxi-

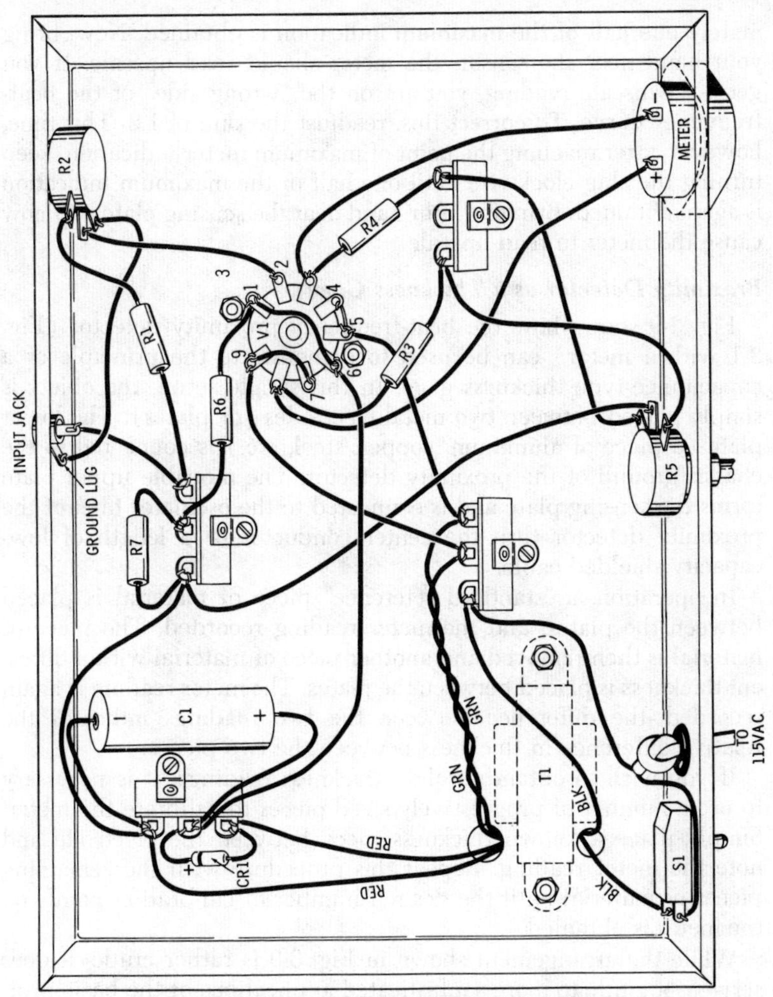

Fig. 3-8. Pictorial diagram for Fig. 3-7.

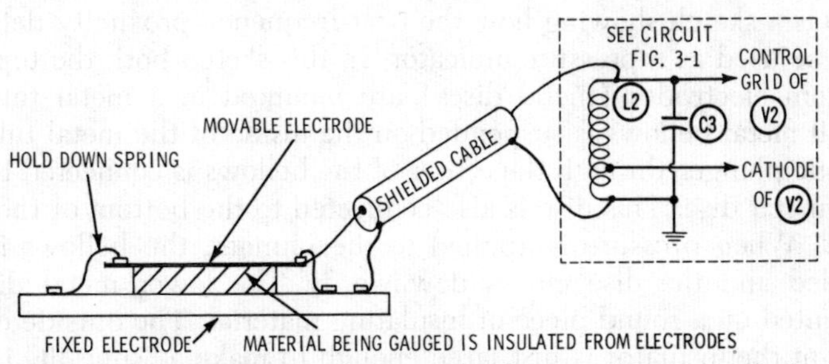

Fig. 3-9. The connection of a proximity detector (Fig. 3-1 or 3-6) to a thickness gage.

mately one half of the maximum indication is obtained. Now, bring your hand near the sensor—the meter should read upscale. If you get a downscale reading, you are on the "wrong side" of the beat-frequency curve. To correct this, readjust the slug of L2. This time, however, after reaching the point of maximum meter indication, keep turning the slug clockwise until one half of the maximum indication is again obtained. Bringing your hand near the sensing plate will now cause the meter to read upscale.

Proximity Detector as a Thickness Gage

Fig. 3-9 shows how the beat-frequency proximity detector (Fig. 3-1 with a meter) can be used to demonstrate the principle of a capacitance-type thickness gage. In this simple setup, the object is simply placed between two metal electrodes (or plates). The lower plate (a piece of aluminum, copper, steel, etc.) is connected to the chassis ground of the proximity detector. The movable upper plate forms the sensing plate and is connected to the oscillator tank of the proximity detector thru the center conductor of a length of low-capacity shielded cable.

In operation, a "standard reference" piece of material is placed between the plates, and the meter reading recorded. The piece of material is then removed and another piece of material with a different thickness is placed between the plates. The meter reading is again recorded—the difference between the two readings indicates the relative difference in thickness between the two pieces.

If you wish to obtain absolute thickness readings, it is necessary to use a number of progressively sized pieces to calibrate the meter. Simply place a known thickness piece between the electrode and note the meter reading. Repeat this procedure with the remaining pieces of material until the desired number of calibration points on the meter is obtained.

While the arrangement shown in Fig. 3-9 is rather crude, it does serve as a guide to more sophisticated applications of the basic principle of beat-frequency proximity detectors. For the example, Fig. 3-10 is a sketch showing how the beat-frequency proximity detector can be used as a pressure indicator. In this sketch both the top and bottom electrodes (metal discs) are mounted in a metal tube. A small metal bellows is suspended on the inside of the metal tube. A plastic plunger through the center of the bellows is connected to the top metal disc. This disc is also connected to the bottom of the bellows. When pressure is applied to the plunger, the bellows is extended and the disc moves downwards. The lower metal disc is mounted on a round piece of insulating material. The outside diameter of the insulator is just large enough to make a "snug fit" in the bottom portion of the tube. A lead through the center of the in-

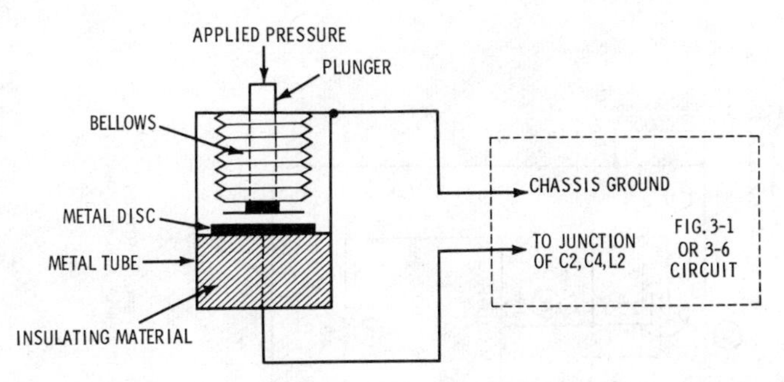

Fig. 3-10. The connection of a pressure transducer to the proximity detector of Fig. 3-1.

sulator is attached to the bottom metal disc, while a second lead is attached to the metal casing. The lead from the bottom metal disc is connected to the sensor terminal (junction of C2 and C4) on the proximity detector chassis, and the lead from the metal casing goes to the chassis ground.

As pressure is applied to the plunger, the metal disc on the lower end of the bellows comes closer to the bottom insulated metal disc; thus, the capacitance between the disc at the bottom of the bellows and the lower metal disc increases. This change in capacitance changes the frequency of the variable-frequency oscillator, and consequently changes the i-f frequency.

Proximity Detector as a Moisture Indicator

The setup shown in Fig. 3-9 can also be used to indicate the amount of moisture in various substances. To demonstrate this function, place a flat sponge about an inch or so thick between the bottom and top plates. Turn on the proximity detector and note the meter indication with the dry sponge between the two plates. Next, slowly add water to the sponge—a few drops at a time. As water is added, you will note that the meter indication changes, indicating a change in the capacitance.

The reason for this apparent change in capacitance is due to the change in the dielectric constant (wet sponge instead of a dry sponge).

FOUR-STAGE F-M DISCRIMINATOR PROXIMITY DETECTOR

We are now going to analyze a proximity detector circuit. (Fig. 3-11), that is less complex and yet has all the advantages of the preceding beat-frequency circuit (Fig. 3-1). The sensor in this unit can

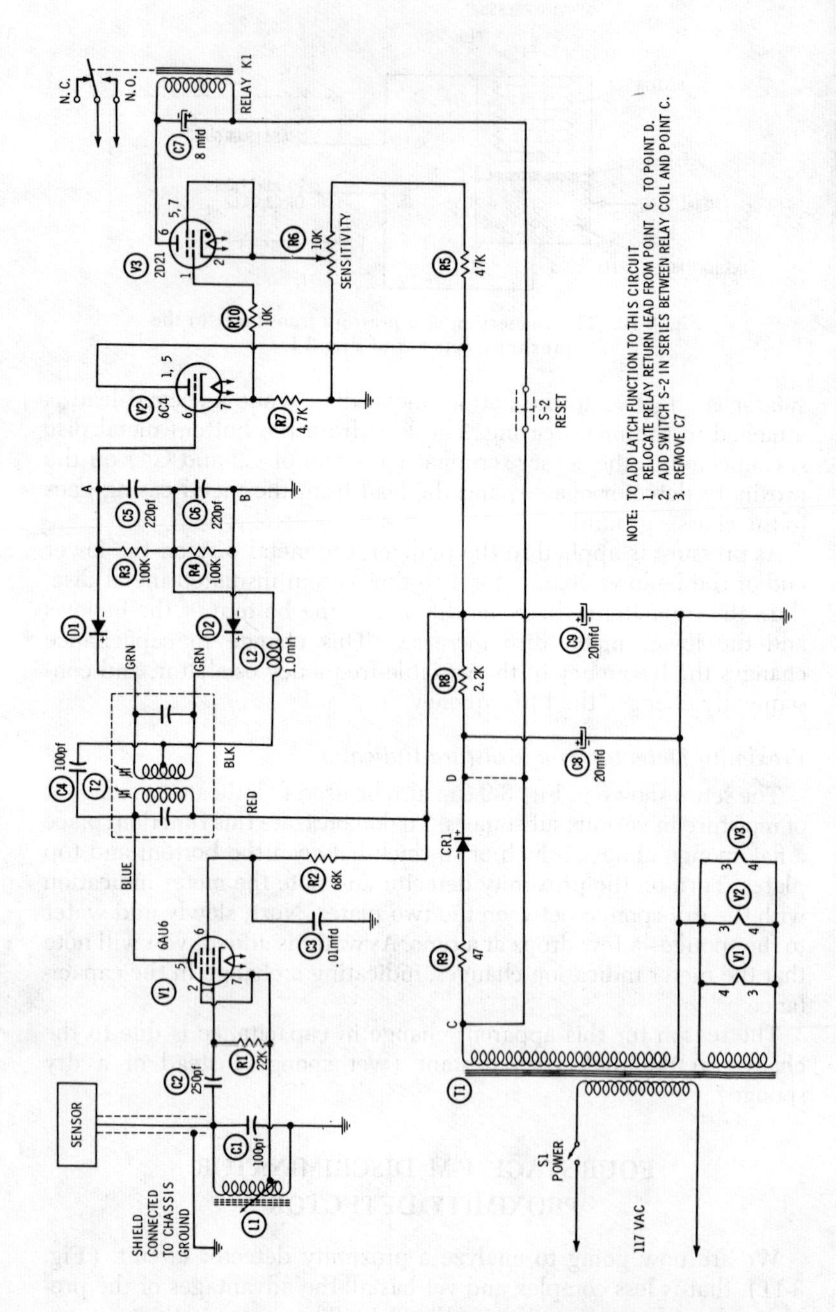

Fig. 3-11. A four-stage, f-m discriminator proximity detector.

Parts List for Fig. 3-11

Item	Description
C1	Capacitor, 100 pf, mica
C2	Capacitor, 250 pf, mica
C3	Capacitor, .01 mfd, paper
C4	Capacitor, 100 pf, mica
C5, C6	Capacitors, 220 pf, mica
C7	Capacitor, 8 mfd, 150v, electrolytic
C8, C9	Capacitors, 20 mfd, 150v, electrolytic
CR1	Rectifier, silicon, 1N2484 or equiv.
D1, D2	Diodes, IN34A, crystal
K1	Relay, 5000 ohm d-c coil, spdt contacts, Potter Brumfield RS5D or equiv.
L1	Coil, antenna, ferrite core, J. W. Miller no. 9012 or equiv.
L2	Choke, r-f, 10 mh
R1	Resistor, 22K, ½ watt
R2	Resistor, 68K, ½ watt
R3, R4	Resistors, 100K, ½ watt
R5	Resistor, 47K, ½ watt
R6	Potentiometer, 10K, 1 watt, wirewound
R7	Resistor, 4.7K, ½ watt
R8	Resistor, 2.2K, 1 watt
R9	Resistor, 47K, ½ watt
R10	Resistor, 10K, ½ watt
S1	Switch, toggle, spst
S2	Switch, push button, normally closed, spst, Grayhill 30-2 or equiv.
T1	Transformer, power, pri. 117v, sec. no. 1 125v @ 50 ma, sec. no. 2 6.3v @ 2 amp
T2	Transformer, 455-kc i-f, center-tapped secondary, Meissner 16-6758 or equiv.
V1	Tube, 6AU6
V2	Tube, 6C4
V3	Tube, 2D21

also be remotely located (5 to 6 ft. maximum) from the chassis and a meter can be substituted for the relay.

Circuit Description

Fig. 3-11 is the schematic of the discriminator-type proximity detector. This circuit requires 25 percent less components than the beat-frequency circuit.

Tube V1, and its associated components (L1, C1, C2, and R1) form a Hartley oscillator. The resting frequency of this oscillator is preset by the adjustment of the slug on L1. The primary of discriminator transformer T2 in the plate circuit of V1 is also tuned to the oscillator resting frequency.

The secondary winding of T2, D1, D2, L2, C5, C6, R3, and R4 form a ratio detector discriminator circuit. A linear output voltage is developed across points A and B (of ratio detector) in proportion to changes in the frequency—above and below the preset resting frequency of the Hartley-oscillator stage. To see just what we mean by this statement, look at Fig. 3-12, which shows the output voltage versus frequency characteristics of the discriminator circuit.

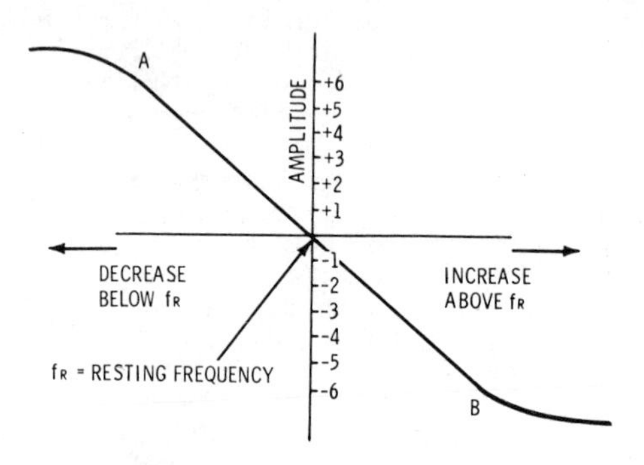

Fig. 3-12. Discriminator characteristics.

When the parallel tank circuit, which includes the secondary of discriminator transformer T2, is tuned to the resting frequency, the discriminator develops zero output voltage. If we decrease the frequency of the oscillator below the resting frequency, the amplitude of the discriminator output voltage will rise in a positive direction. An increase in the oscillator frequency above the rest frequency causes the amplitude of discriminator-output voltage to swing in a negative direction.

Notice that between points A and B, the curve is quite linear; that is, the output voltage of the discriminator is proportional to the frequency change applied to the discriminator. Beyond points A and B, the curve rounds off, indicating that the output voltage of the discriminator is no longer proportional to the frequency change.

Now we will return to the schematic of Fig. 3-11. The d-c output voltage from the discriminator is applied to the grid of the cathode-follower stage. The purpose of this cathode-follower stage is to isolate the high-impedance output of the discriminator from the low-impedance control-grid circuit of V3.

The d-c bias voltage developed across cathode resistor R7 of V2 is determined by the output of the discriminator.

This bias voltage is also present at the control grid of V3 (due to its direct connection to the cathode of V2) and must be cancelled out to prevent V3 from firing when the output from the discriminator is zero volts. This is accomplished by adjusting the sensitivity control until the positive voltage on cathode of V3 overrides the static positive voltage developed at the control grid of V3 when the proximity detector oscillator is at the resting frequency.

We will now examine the operation of the circuit in greater detail. With a sensor (without an object in its vicinity) connected to the oscillator (Fig. 3-11), the slug in L1 is adjusted to the resting frequency. Under these conditions, the output voltage of the discriminator will be zero, and V3 will not fire.

As an object approaches the sensor, the capacitance between the sensor and ground will increase. This increase in capacitance appears across tank circuit L1-C1 of oscillator V1, and the oscillator frequency decreases below the preset resting frequency. This decrease in oscillator frequency will appear as a decrease in the frequency at the secondary of T2, and will produce a positive output voltage from the discriminator (Fig. 3-12).

This positive output voltage appears at the control grid of V2 and the effective grid bias on V2 decreases. This causes a simultaneous increase in the positive voltage at the cathode of V2 and at the control grid of V3; it also causes V3 to fire and energize the relay. Since V3 is supplied with an a-c plate voltage, it ceases firing when its positive control grid voltage is removed (when the object leaves the vicinity of the sensor).

A length of shielded cable is used to connect the sensor to the oscillator. Since the total value of the oscillator tank-circuit capacitance is 250 picofarads, for a resting frequency of 455 kc, the total combined value of the lead-in cable capacitance and the C1 capacitance cannot exceed this value. For example, if the capacitance of a four foot length of RG59 cable is approximately 84 pf (4×21 pf) then the required value of the fixed capacitor (C1) would be $250 - 84$ or 166 picofarad. In the circuit of Fig. 3-11, the value of C1 was selected as 100 pf to provide more adjustment range for L1.

Construction

Since the construction of this discriminator proximity detector is straightforward, you can make your own parts layout. The routing and length of the wiring in the oscillator circuit is critical—especially V1 and its associated components. The pictorial diagram for this circuit is shown in Fig. 3-13.

Components can be substituted as follows: V1 (6SK7, 6AU6, or 6AH6); V2 (6C4, 6C5, or ½ of a 12AU7), V3 (5727 or 2050), C2 (100 pf to 500 pf), C3 (0.01 mfd to 0.1 mfd), C7 (8 mfd to 20 mfd) and C8 and C9 (8 mfd to 20 mfd). The tube socket must be replaced when an octal tube is used instead of a miniature type.

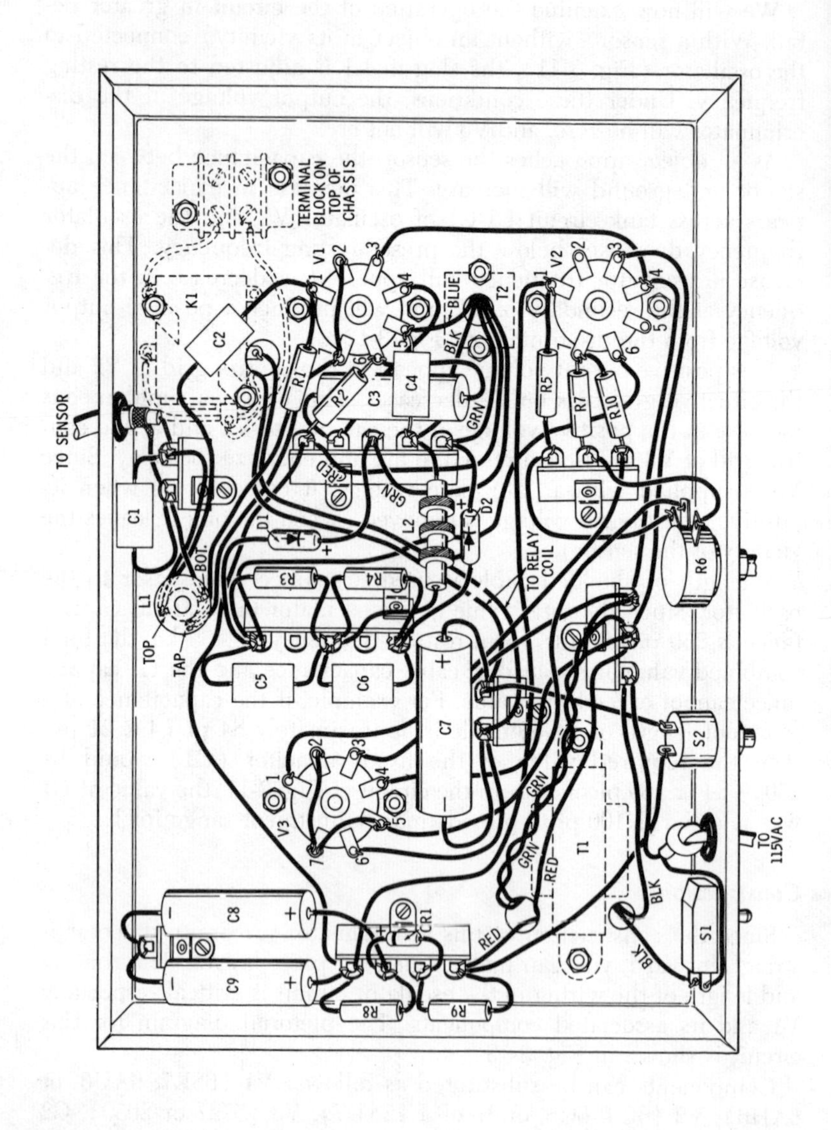

Fig. 3-13. Pictorial diagram for Fig. 3-11.

Adjustment

After checking the completed unit for any errors, connect a sensor and apply a-c line power to the circuit. For the initial adjustment, remove V3 from its socket and connect either a 20,000 ohm/volt multimeter or vtvm to the discriminator output (between points A and B, as shown in Fig. 3-11). After allowing about 5 minutes for the circuit to stabilize, adjust the oscillator to the 455-kc resting frequency. There are several procedures for setting the resting frequency. If you have access to an r-f signal generator tunable to 455 kc and an oscilloscope, connect the high side of the signal-generator output through a 10-megohm resistor to the high side of the oscilloscope vertical amplifier. Connect the low side of the signal-generator output to the low side of the oscilloscope input. The procedure is illustrated in Fig. 3-14. Tune the generator to 455 kc and adjust the sweep frequency control of the oscilloscope until 8 or 10 complete cycles are displayed on the scope tube. Disconnect the r-f generator and connect the high-side lead of the oscilloscope to the oscillator tank (Fig. 3-14) and low-side lead to the chassis ground. Adjust the slug of L1 until an identical number of cycles again appear on the oscilloscope. If you do not have access to an r-f signal generator, an ordinary a-m radio can be used to calibrate the oscillator. With both the proximity detector and the radio operating, bring the radio to within approximately 6 inches of oscillator coil L1. Tune the radio to exactly 910 kc, the second harmonic of 455 kc. Adjust the slug of L1 until the signal is heard on the radio. When calibrating the oscillator in this manner, be sure the dial of the radio is accurately calibrated, otherwise the oscillator calibration will be inaccurate. The receiver calibration can be easily verified by tuning in the fre-

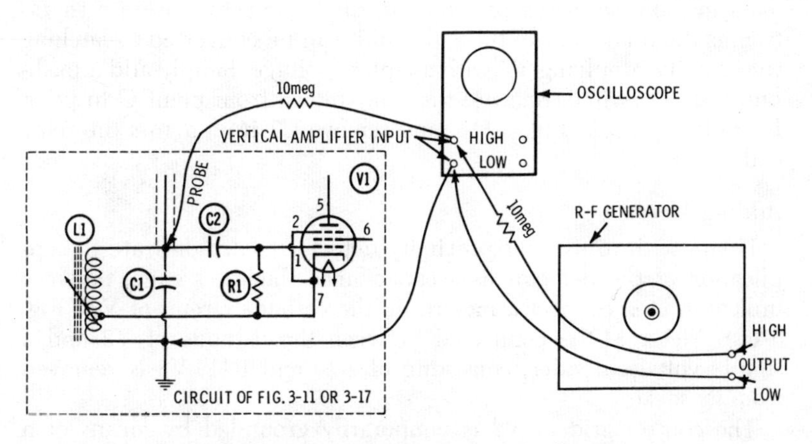

Fig. 3-14. A method of calibrating an oscillator stage.

quency of a known broadcast station, and checking the dial of the radio for the same frequency indication.

After you have set the oscillator to 455 kc, the next step is to adjust the tank circuit of the discriminator (T2 secondary). Adjust the slug in the tank circuit (in T2 secondary) until a null is indicated by the vtvm across the discriminator output. As this adjustment is made, the meter will first indicate a positive voltage, swing through zero, and then read a negative voltage. (If zero-center meter is not available, reverse the meter leads for the negative voltage reading.)

After adjusting the T2 secondary for a null (zero on the meter), the next step is the adjustment of the T2 primary winding tank circuit. Temporarily detune the secondary of T2 until a reading is obtained on the meter—either a positive or negative output voltage will be satisfactory. Adjust the slug of the primary winding of T2 for a maximum reading (primary T2 is now tuned for 455-kc signal), after this is obtained, retune the discriminator tank circuit (T2 secondary) for a null in output voltage as described in the previous paragraph.

With the meter still connected, bring your hand close to the sensor. The output voltage of the discriminator should increase in a positive direction on the vtvm. If a negative output voltage is obtained, it will be necessary to reverse the output connections of the discriminator. To do this, simply interchange the point A connection to the control grid of V2 and point B connection to the chassis ground.

Disconnect the vtvm, and replace V3 in its socket. Bringing your hand close to the sensor should now cause V3 to fire and energize the relay.

Adding Latch Control

As in the case of the previous proximity detectors using a thyratron as the relay control tube, this unit can be converted to latching function by supplying V3 with a-c plate voltage. Simply add a push-button reset switch, relocate the relay-return from point C to point D (dotted lines in Fig. 3-11), and remove C7 from across the relay coil.

Adding Meter

If you wish to use this proximity detector to demonstrate the application of the detector as a capacitance thickness gage, pressure indicator, etc., connect a meter into the cathode circuit of V2 (Fig. 3-15). Meter M2 is connected between the cathode of V2 and a simple voltage divider, consisting of R10 and R11. V3 is removed from its socket.

The control grid of V2 is temporarily grounded by means of a jumper, and meter adjustment (R11) is set for a zero meter reading.

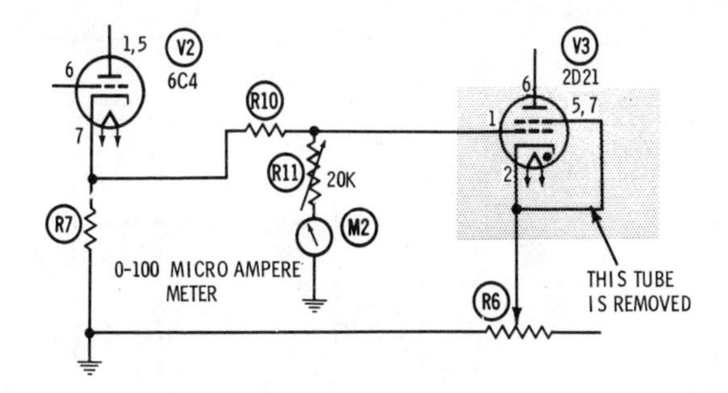

Fig. 3-15. A suggested method for connecting a simple indicator into the circuit of Fig. 3-11.

The jumper is disconnected, and the proximity detector is ready for operation. If the meter should read backwards when your hand is brought near the sensor, simply reverse the meter connections.

If you have a vtvm on hand, you can use it instead of the setup just described. Simply connect the positive probe to the cathode of V2 and the negative probe to chassis ground. With the control grid of V2 temporarily grounded, adjust the "zero adjust" control of the vtvm for a zero meter reading. Remove the ground from the grid of V2, and the proximity detector is ready for operation.

FOUR-STAGE BALANCED-REACTANCE PROXIMITY DETECTOR

This is an interesting circuit which operates on the principle of two equal reactances across a constant frequency source. When additional capacitance is shunted across the capacitive leg of this balanced impedance, Point B will be negative to Point A. This circuit has the advantage of using an oscillator that operates at a constant amplitude and frequency, thus increasing oscillator stability.

Circuit Description

To get an idea of the basic circuit operation look at Fig. 3-16; an r-f generator supplies a 100-kc r-f signal to the primary of coupling transformer T3. The voltage appearing across the secondary of T3 is applied across series-connected RC combination R3-C5. The values of resistance and capacitance are selected so that at 100 kc the capacitive reactance of C5 is equal to the resistance of R3. This being the case, the r-f voltage across R3 will equal the r-f voltage across C5. The r-f voltages appearing across R3 and C5 are rectified by diodes D1 and D2; the resulting pulsating d-c voltage being filtered and stored by R4, R5, C6, and C7.

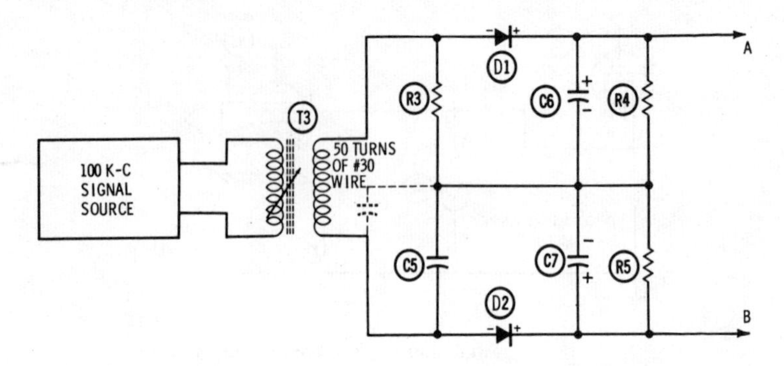

Fig. 3-16. The basic circuit of a balanced reactance proximity detector.

Assume that the top of the secondary winding of T3 is positive, D1 will conduct and charge C6 to the polarity indicated on Fig. 3-16. On the next alternation of the signal, the bottom of secondary winding is positive, and D2 conducts and charges C7 to polarily indicated on Fig. 3-16. The voltage across R4 and R5 in series measured at A and B will be zero because the voltage drops across R4 and R5 are equal and opposite and cancel out.

Now, assume we increase the effective capacitance of C5 by adding the external capacitance, as indicated by the dashed lines. This will decrease the effective reactance of C5, and less r-f voltage will appear across C5 than across R3. Consequently, the output voltage from D2 will be lower than that from D1, with the result that a voltage differential appears between the points A and B—point A is positive with respect to point B. On the other hand, a decrease in the capacitance of C5 will result in an increase in the reactance. This increased reactance will cause a larger value of r-f voltage to be developed across C5 than R3 and point B will become more positive than point A.

With the basic understanding of the circuit under your belt, look at a complete circuit (Fig. 3-17). The 100-kc oscillator consists of V1, its associated components L1, C1, C2, R1, C3, R2, and the primary of the coupling transformer T3. The 100-kc r-f signal developed at the primary of T3 is coupled to the secondary, where it is applied across the balancing potentiometer (R3) and capacitor C5. Diodes D1 and D2 rectify the r-f voltage appearing across R3 and C5 and produce a d-c output voltage across points A and B, as explained earlier. This voltage is applied to the control grid of cathode follower V2. This stage converts the relatively high impedance across points A and B to the low impedance of thyratron V3.

The voltage developed across the V2 cathode resistor (R6) varies in proportion to the signal applied to the input of the tube. Since

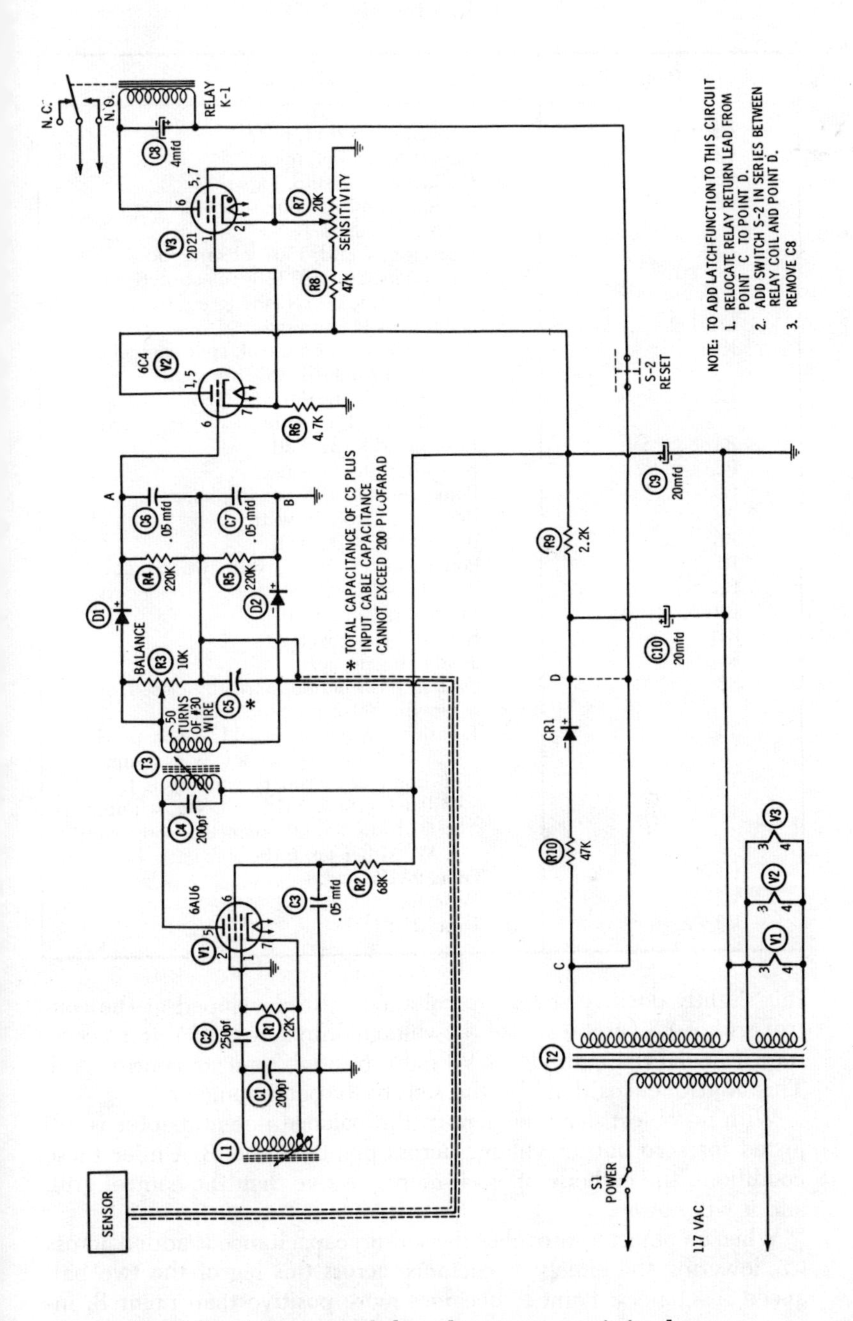

Fig. 3-17. A four-stage, balanced-reactance proximity detector.

Parts List for Fig. 3-17

Item	Description
C1, C4	Capacitors, 200 pf, mica
C2	Capacitor, 250 pf, mica
C3, C6, C7	Capacitors, .05 mfd, paper
C5	Capacitor, mica, value selected (see schematic)
C8	Capacitor, 4 mfd, 150v, electrolytic
C9, C10	Capacitors, 20 mfd, 150v, electrolytic
CR1	Rectifier, silicon, 1N2484 or equiv.
D1, D2	Diodes, IN34A, crystal
K1	Relay, 5000 ohm d-c coil, spdt contacts, Potter Brumfield RS5D or equiv.
L1	Coil, antenna, ferrite core, J.W. Miller 6314, or equiv.
R1	Resistor, 22K, ½ watt
R2	Resistor, 68K, ½ watt
R3	Potentiometer, 10K, 1 watt, linear taper
R4, R5	Resistors, 220K, ½ watt
R6	Resistor, 4.7K, ½ watt
R7	Potentiometer, 20K, 1 watt, wirewound
R8	Resistor, 47K, ½ watt
R9	Resistor, 2.2K, 1 watt
R10	Resistor, 47, ½ watt
S1	Switch, toggle, spst
S2	Switch, push button, normally closed, spst, Grayhill 30-2 or equiv.
T1	Transformer, power, pri. 117v, sec. no. 1 125 @ 50 ma, sec. no. 2 6.3v @ 2 amp
T3	Coil, iron core (Primary winding is J. W. Miller type no. 6314 coil, sec. winding is 50 turns no. 30 enameled wire over J. W. Miller no. 6314 coil.)
V1	Tube, 6AU6
V2	Tube, 6C4
V3	Tube, 2D21

this slightly positive static d-c voltage is also developed at the control grid of V3 (as a result of the voltage drop across R6), it is necessary to make the cathode of V3 more positive than its control grid. This adjustment is done by the sensitivity potentiometer.

With no object near the sensor, the balance potentiometer is adjusted for zero output voltage across points A and B. Under these conditions, the cathode of V3 is more positive than the control grid, and it will not fire.

When an object approaches the sensor, capacitance is added across C5, lowering the effective reactance across this leg of the two balanced reactances. Point A becomes more positive than point B, increasing the positive voltage applied to the input of V2. The cathode of V2 then becomes more positive than its cathode. V3 will fire and energize the relay. Since V3 is operated with an a-c plate supply, it will cease firing as soon as the positive control grid voltage is removed—when the object is removed from the vicinity of the sensor.

Construction

Like the previous proximity detectors, this unit can be built on a chassis of your own choice. Be sure to keep short leads in the oscillator portion of the circuit (V1, L1, T3, etc.). Fig. 3-18 is the pictorial diagram of this circuit.

The total capacitance of the capacitive-reactance leg of the series-connected RC combination (R3, C5) cannot exceed 200 picofarad. If the shielded-coaxial cable has a capacitance of 100 pf then the value of C5 is 100 pf (200 − 100 pf).

Components can be substituted as follows: V1 (6SJ7), V2 (½ 12AU7, or 6C5), V3 (2050), C2 (250 pf to 500 pf), C8 (4 mfd to 20 mfd), R6 (2.2K to 4.7K) and R7 (10K to 50K). The tube socket must be replaced when the octal tube is used instead of the miniature tube.

Adjustment

After checking the unit for any errors, remove V3 from its socket and connect either a vtvm or 20,000-ohms/volt vom between point A and B. Apply a-c power and adjust the tuning slug of L1 until the oscillator is tuned to 100-kc.

There are several possible ways to adjust the oscillator frequency to 100 kc. If you have an audio or r-f generator capable of tuning to 100 kc, connect the high side of the signal-generator output through a 10-megohm resistor to the high side of an oscilloscope vertical amplifier, and connect the low side of signal-generator output to the low side of the oscilloscope input (Fig. 3-14). With the audio generator set to 100 kc, adjust the sweep frequency control of the oscilloscope for a display of 8 or 10 cycles (depending on the number of vertical divisions on the graticule of the oscilloscope). Disconnect the signal generator, and connect the high-side lead to the sensor terminal (junctions C1 and C2) and the low-side lead to chassis ground. Adjust the slug of L1 until an identical number of cycles appears on the oscilloscope; the oscillator is now tuned to 100 kc. Actually, it is not critical that the oscillator be set to exactly 100-kc; a variation of ± 10% is acceptable since the balance potentiometer (R3) can be adjusted to compensate for a small variance in the input (oscillator) frequency.

If you do not have access to an audio generator, the oscillator can be calibrated with a broadcast-band radio. With both the radio and the proximity detector turned on, adjust the slug of L1 until the

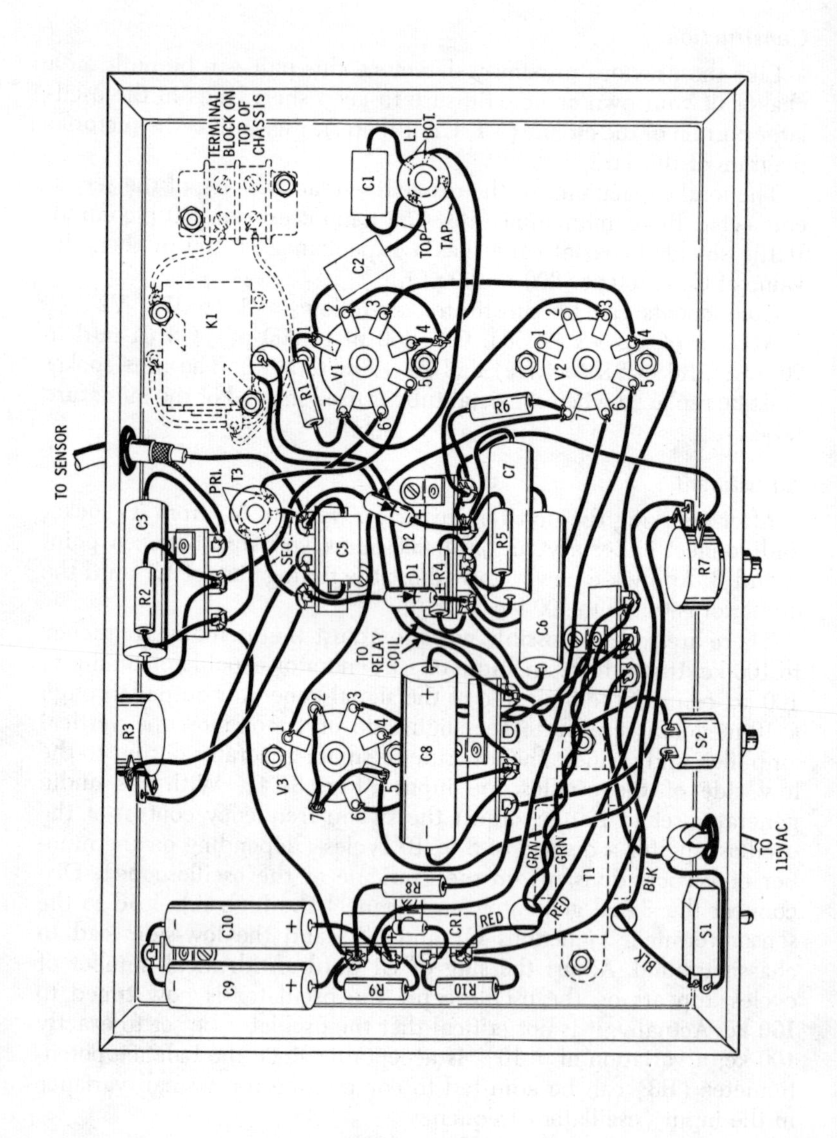

Fig. 3-18. Pictorial diagram for Fig. 3-17.

harmonics of the signal from the oscillator can be tuned in at 100-kc intervals on the radio dial. For example, if the oscillator is correctly adjusted, the oscillator signal will be received at 600, 700, 800, etc. on the radio dial. It is important to check at every 100-kc interval rather than at just one point on the dial (say 600 kc). For instance, if the proximity-detector oscillator was incorrectly set at 200 kc, its signal could still be received at 600 kc on the radio (third harmonic of 200 kc).

After the oscillator is adjusted to 100 kc, the next step is to set the balance potentiometer for a zero reading on a meter connected across points A and B. With the sensor connected, but without an object in the vicinity of sensor, adjust the balance potentiometer for a zero meter indication. You will notice that as this adjustment is made, the meter will indicate a positive voltage, zero, and then a negative voltage (or vice versa), depending on the setting of R3.

With R3 set for a zero meter reading, disconnect the meter and place V3 in its socket. Temporarily connect a jumper from the control grid of V2 to ground (B −), and adjust the sensitivity potentiometer to the point where V3 does not fire. Disconnect the jumper, and the unit is ready for operation. Bringing your hand near the sensing plate should cause V3 to fire and energize the relay.

Adding Latch Function

Should you wish to add the latching function, add a reset switch (S2), and connect the lower end of the relay coil to point D as indicated by the dashed lines in Fig. 3-17. Remove C8.

Chapter 4

Transistorized Proximity Detectors

The circuits in this chapter are completely transistorized and offer the advantages of small size and low power consumption. The use of transistors in proximity detectors opens up a number of new applications since these circuits do not require a-c power for operation. Thus, a battery-powered transistor proximity detector can be located outdoors away from power lines. The small physical size of transistors compared to vacuum tubes makes possible the construction of much smaller proximity detectors—an advantage if the detector is to be concealed from view. Also, since transistors generate less heat, they can be packaged closely with other components. This fact also aids in the miniaturization of transistorized proximity detectors.

THREE-STAGE LOADED-OSCILLATOR TOUCHSWITCH

Fig. 4-1 shows the schematic of a simple, two-transistor, proximity detector that can be used as a "touchswitch." Essentially, this circuit is the transistor counterpart of the single-stage, vacuum-tube, "loaded-oscillator" capacity relay.

Unlike its vacuum-tube counterpart, a relay will not respond to the small current changes in the collector circuit of the transistorized proximity detector. Instead, it is necessary to rectify a portion of the r-f voltage developed by its oscillator. The existance of this voltage depends on whether the oscillator circuit is resonant or nonresonant. This rectified voltage is used to drive a relay-control transistor.

Circuit Description

The basic "loaded-oscillator" circuit consists of Q1, L1, L2, C1, C2, C3, R1, and R2 in Fig. 4-1. Feedback capacitor C2 is adjusted (without an object near the sensor) until Q1 is oscillating. Under these

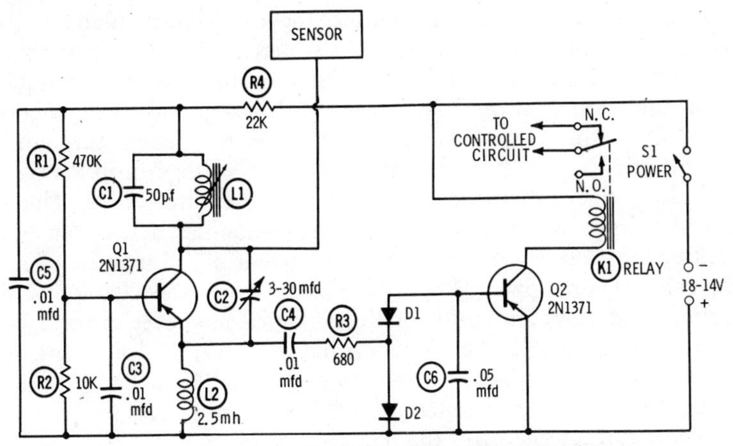

Fig. 4-1. A three-stage, loaded-oscillator proximity detector.

Parts List for Fig. 4-1

Item	Description
C1	Capacitor, 50 pf, mica
C2	Capacitor, 3-30 pf, trimmer
C3, C4, C5	Capacitors, 0.01 mfd, paper, Goodall 663UW or equiv.
C6	Capacitor, 0.05 mfd, paper, Goodall 663UW or equiv.
D1, D2	Diodes, IN34A, crystal
K1	Relay, 5000 ohm d-c coil, spdt contacts, Potter Brumfield RS5D or equiv.
L1	Coil, ferrite core, antenna, J. W. Miller no. 4506 or equiv.
L2	Choke, r-f, 2.5 mh
Q1, Q2	Transistors, 2N1371
R1	Resistor, 470K, ½ watt
R2	Resistor, 10K, ½ watt
R3	Resistor, 680, ½ watt
R4	Resistor, 22K, ½ watt
S1	Switch, toggle, spst

conditions, an r-f voltage is developed across emitter r-f choke L2. This voltage is applied to the voltage doubler rectifier (D1, D2, and C6) via isolating resistor R3 coupling capacitor C4.

The voltage doubler produces a negative output voltage which is proportional to the r-f voltage developed by the loaded oscillator. This negative voltage is applied to the base of Q2 and forward biases this transistor until its collector current is sufficient to energize the relay.

When an object nears the sensor, the capacitance increases between the sensor and the object. This increased capacitance shunts tank circuit L1-C1 and decreases the amplitude of the r-f voltage in the tank circuit at the collector of Q1. Consequently, the junction-bias voltages of Q1 are reduced and the emitter current through L2 is reduced. This emitter current reduces the voltage drop across L2 and also reduces the negative voltage at the emitter of Q1. This reduced voltage is applied via the voltage doubler across the base-emitter junction of Q2. The collector current of Q2 is reduced, and the relay de-energizes. When the object leaves the vicinity of the sensing plate, the amplitude of the r-f signal increases in the L1-C1 tank of oscillator V1. The junction biases on Q1 will increase, and this increases the emitter current through L2. The negative voltage across the base emitter junction of Q2 is restored, and its increased collector current energizes the relay.

Construction

The three-stage proximity detector is assembled on a piece of perforated phenolic board. The tie-points for the various components are made to small terminals inserted through holes in the perforated board. The placement of parts is not critical, except that L1 and L2 should be kept fairly well separated. The pictorial diagram (Fig. 4-2) shows this arrangement.

Components can be substituted as follows: R1 may range from 220K to 470K, R2 (10K to 15K), R3 (470 ohms to 1K), C4 (0.01 mfd to 0.1 mfd), C6 (0.01 mfd to 0.1 mfd), C5 (0.01 mfd to 0.1 mfd), and L2 (2.5 mh to 5 mh), Q1 and Q2 (2N404A, 2N1192, 2N1373, 2N1375, or 2N1377).

Adjustment

After checking the unit for any possible wiring errors, connect a sensor without an object in its vicinity and a battery or a power supply to the chassis. After waiting a minute or so for the unit to stabilize, increase the capacity of C2 by turning its adjusting screw clockwise until the relay energizes. Now, slowly decrease the capacity of C2 until the relay just opens. Touching the sensor with a finger should now energize the relay. Increasing the area of the sensing plate will also increase the sensitivity.

THREE-STAGE LOADED-OSCILLATOR PROXIMITY DETECTOR WITH LATCH-CONTROLLED RELAY

As in the case of the vacuum-tube proximity-detector circuits described in Chapters 2 and 3, it is possible to add the latching function to transistorized proximity relays; Fig. 4-3 shows how this is

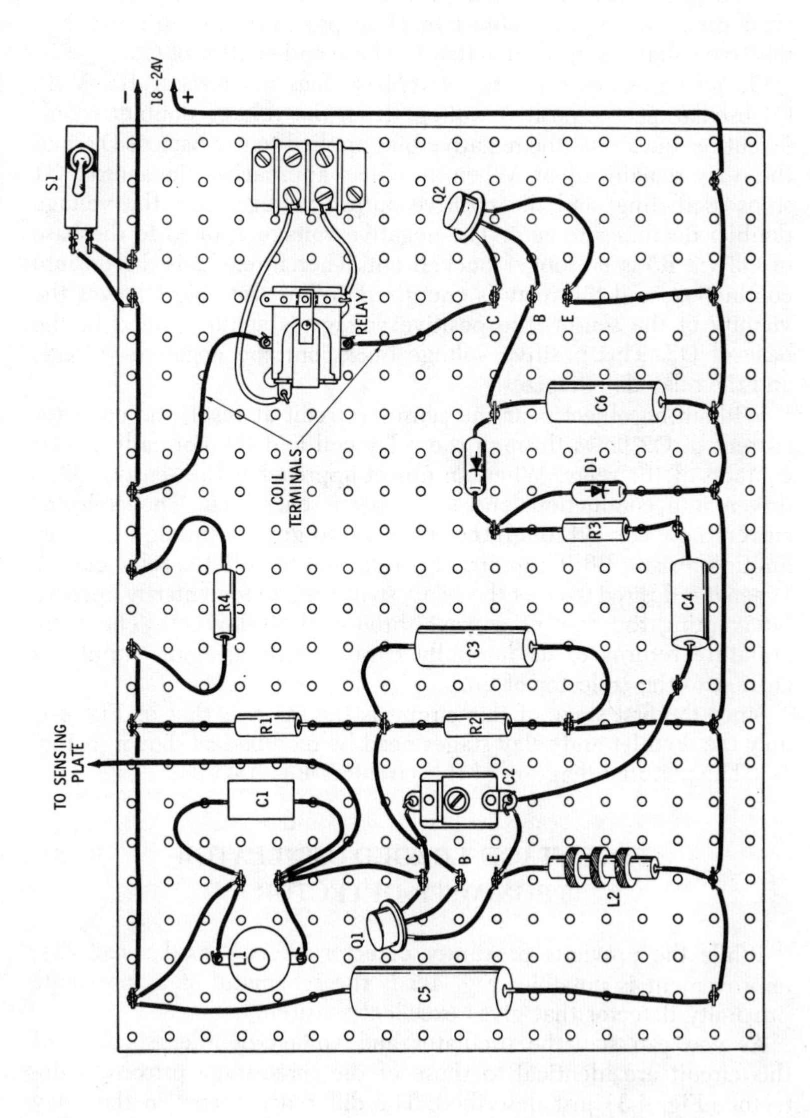

Fig. 4-2. Pictorial diagram for Fig. 4-1.

done. As you can see, up to the voltage-doubler rectifier section, this circuit is identical to that of Fig. 4-1. Beyond this point, note that the connections to diodes D1 and D2 are reversed to produce a positive output voltage for the appplied r-f voltage. Thus, when Q1 is oscillating (without an object in close proximity to the sensor), a positive voltage is applied across the base and emitter of Q2.

Q2 also receives some negative base bias via resistor R5. With Q1 oscillating, the positive voltage from the voltage doubler is sufficient to "buck out" the negative bias applied to the base of Q2, and the relay remains open. When an object approaches the sensor, Q1 stops oscillating, and the positive output voltage from the voltage doubler decreases to zero. The negative voltage applied to the base of Q2 via R5 is no longer bucked out. Therefore, Q2 is driven into conduction, and the relay is energized. When the object leaves the vicinity of the sensor, the positive voltage is again applied to the base of Q2. This positive voltage bucks out the negative voltage, and the relay de-energizes.

Without an object near the sensor (circuit at rest), the collector current of Q2 flows through the relay coil and the normally closed contacts of the relay. When an object approaches the sensor, Q2 is driven into conduction, and the relay is energized. The collector current now flows through the relay coil to ground through current-limiting resistor R6. This current is sufficient to hold the relay closed. When it is desired to reset the relay, switch S2 is momentarily opened, interrupting the flow of current through the relay coil. The relay armature returns to its normally closed position, again supplying current to the collector of Q2.

Since the first stage of this circuit is the same as that of Fig. 4-1, only the doubler and relay stages need be modified as shown in Fig. 4-3. The pictorial diagram of this circuit is Fig. 4-4.

FOUR-STAGE LOADED-OSCILLATOR PROXIMITY DETECTOR

While the previous proximity detector offered good sensitivity, improvement is possible. Fig. 4-5 is the schematic of a four-stage proximity detector that gives excellent sensitivity.

As you can see, the oscillator and voltage-doubler sections of this circuit are identical to those of the three-stage proximity detector (Fig. 4-3) just described. The difference occurs in the relay control stage where a third transistor is added to increase the current gain. The increased current gain of this stage permits the relay to respond to smaller changes in the base bias applied to Q2. Thus, a smaller change in capacitance between the sensing plate and ground

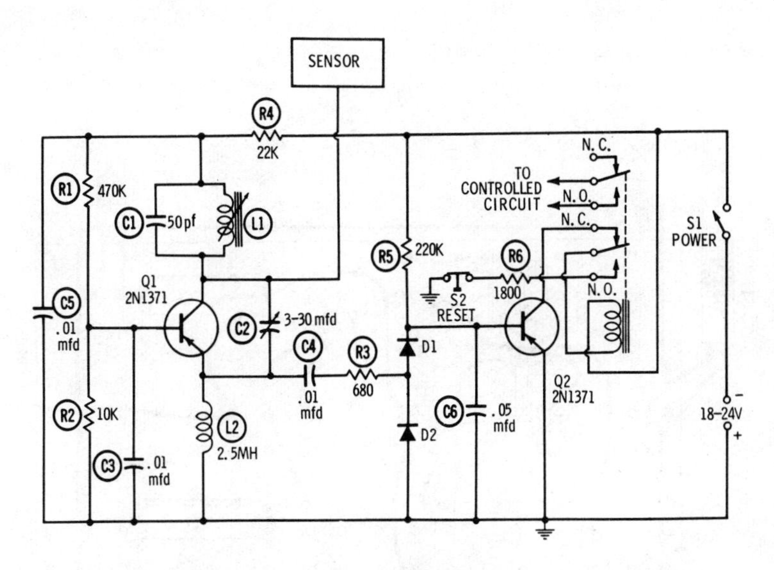

Fig. 4-3. A three-stage, loaded-oscillator proximity detector with latch-controlled relay.

Parts List for Fig. 4-3

Item	Description
C1	Capacitor, 50 pf, mica
C2	Capacitor, 3-30 pf, trimmer
C3, C4, C5	Capacitors, 0.01 mfd, paper, Goodall 663UW or equiv.
C6	Capacitor, 0.05 mfd, paper, Goodall 663UW or equiv.
D1, D2	Diodes, 1N34A crystal
K1	Relay, 5000 ohm d-c coil, dpdt, Potter Brumfield FR11 or equiv.
L1	Coil, ferrite core, antenna, J. W. Miller 4506 or equiv.
L2	Choke, r-f, 2.5 mh
Q1, Q2	Transistors, 2N1371
R1	Resistor, 470K, ½ watt
R2	Resistor, 10K, ½ watt
R3	Resistor, 680, ½ watt
R4	Resistor, 22K, ½ watt
R5	Resistor, 220K, ½ watt
R6	Resistor, 1800, 1 watt
S1	Switch, toggle, spst
S2	Switch, push button, spst, Grayhill 30-2 or equiv.

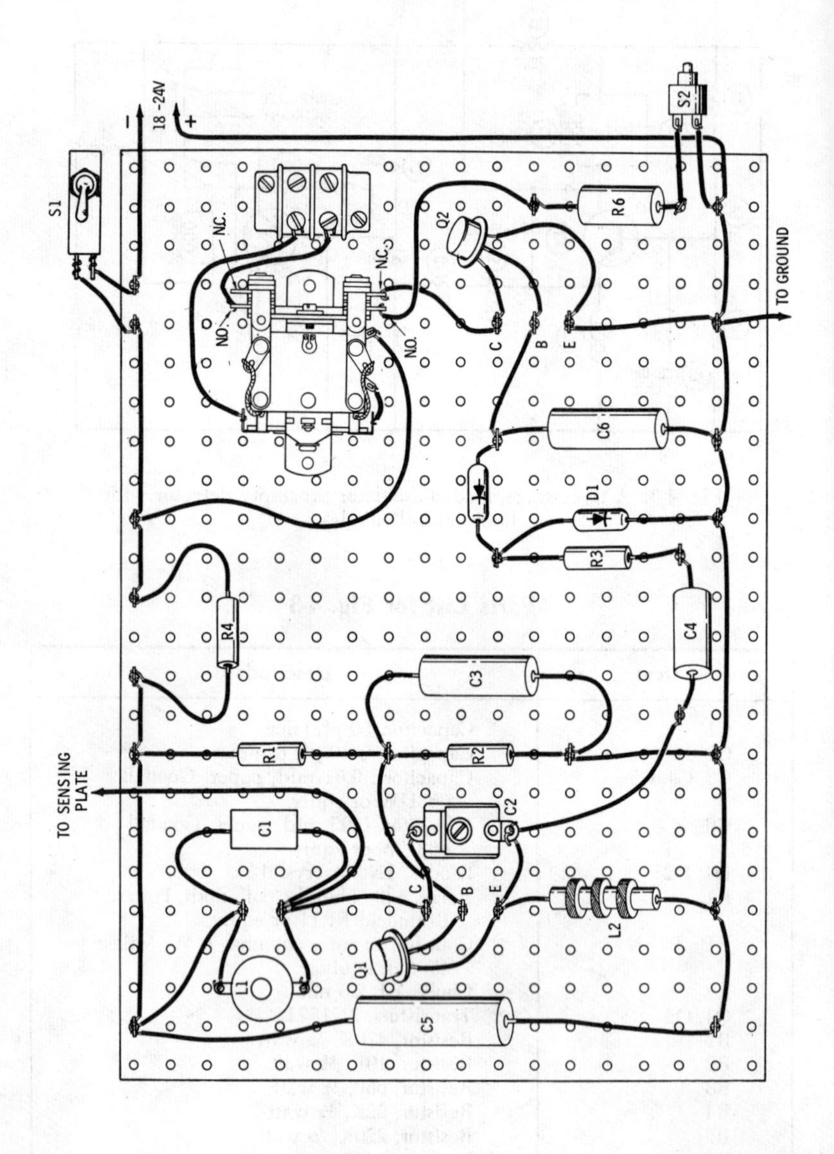

Fig. 4-4. Pictorial diagram for Fig. 4-3.

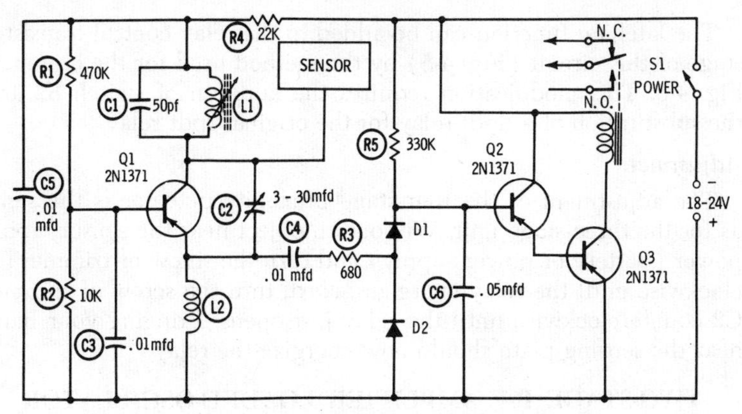

Fig. 4-5. A four-stage, loaded-oscillator proximity detector.

Parts List for Fig. 4-5

Item	Description
C1	Capacitor, 50 pf, mica
C2	Capacitor, 3-30 pf, trimmer
C3, C4, C5	Capacitors, 0.01 mfd, paper, Goodall 663UW or equiv.
C6	Capacitor, .05 mfd, paper, Goodall 663UW or equiv.
D1, D2	Diodes, 1N34A, crystal
K1	Relay, 5000 ohm d-c coil, spst, Potter Brumfield RS5D or equiv.
L1	Coil, ferrite core, antenna, J. W. Miller 4506 or equiv.
L2	Choke, r-f, 2.5 mh
Q1, Q2, Q3	Transistors, 2N1371
R1	Resistor, 470K, ½ watt
R2	Resistor, 10K, ½ watt
R3	Resistor, 470, ½ watt
R4	Resistor, 22K, ½ watt
R5	Resistor, 330K, ½ watt
S1	Switch, toggle, spst

will still be enough to cause a sufficient change in the base bias of Q2 to energize the relay.

Construction

The proximity detector is assembled on a small piece of perforated phenolic board as shown in Fig. 4-6. Construction of this circuit is actually identical to the circuit in Fig. 4-3 without the latching function except for the additional transistor (Q3).

The latching function can be added to the relay control transistor stage of this circuit (Fig. 4-5) by the method used for the circuit in Fig. 4-3. This modification requires the addition of switch S2 and the substitution of a dpdt relay for the original spdt relay.

Adjustment

The adjustment of the four-stage proximity detector is the same as for the three-stage unit. Without an object near the sensor, apply power (battery or power supply) and turn the screw of trimmer C2 clockwise until the relay energizes. Next, turn the screw of trimmer C2 counterclockwise until the relay just opens. Bringing your hand near the sensing plate should now energize the relay.

TWO-STAGE R-F AMPLIFIER LOADED-OSCILLATOR PROXIMITY DETECTOR

In the preceding four-stage proximity detector (Fig. 4-5), sensitivity was improved by an additional d-c amplifier stage. In the circuit in Fig. 4-7 the oscillator signal is amplified before it is rectified, and the temperature-sensitive d-c amplifier Q3 used in the previous circuit (Fig. 4-5) is eliminated.

As you can see from Fig. 4-7, the "loaded-oscillator" portion of this circuit is identical to the previously described circuits (Fig. 4-1, 4-3, 4-5). The r-f voltage (proportional to the amplitude of oscillation in the tank circuit of V1) developed at the emitter of Q1 is applied to the base of Q2. The r-f amplifier stage consists of Q2, R3, R5, R6, R7, and L3. The amplified r-f signal is developed across L3.

The r-f signal appearing at the collector of Q2 is fed to the voltage doubler (C7, D1, D2, and C6). The positive output voltage of the voltage doubler is applied to the base-emitter junction of relay control transistor Q3. This junction also receives a negative voltage developed across r-f amplifier stage Q2 and its emitter resistor (R7).

With no object near the sensor, the output of the voltage doubler is a positive voltage. This positive voltage "bucks out" the negative bias voltage of Q3 obtained from the preceding r-f amplifier stage, and Q3 will not conduct. Consequently, the relay is not energized. When an object approaches the sensor, Q1 stops oscillating, and accordingly, the output of the voltage doubler drops to zero. Without a positive voltage, the base of Q3 becomes negative with respect to its emitter, Q3 will now conduct, and the relay is energized.

Construction

As in the case of the three previous transistorized proximity detectors, this unit is assembled on a piece of perforated phenolic board. In assembling this unit, L1, L2, and L3 must be kept well separated in order to prevent unwanted oscillations caused by inter-coupling

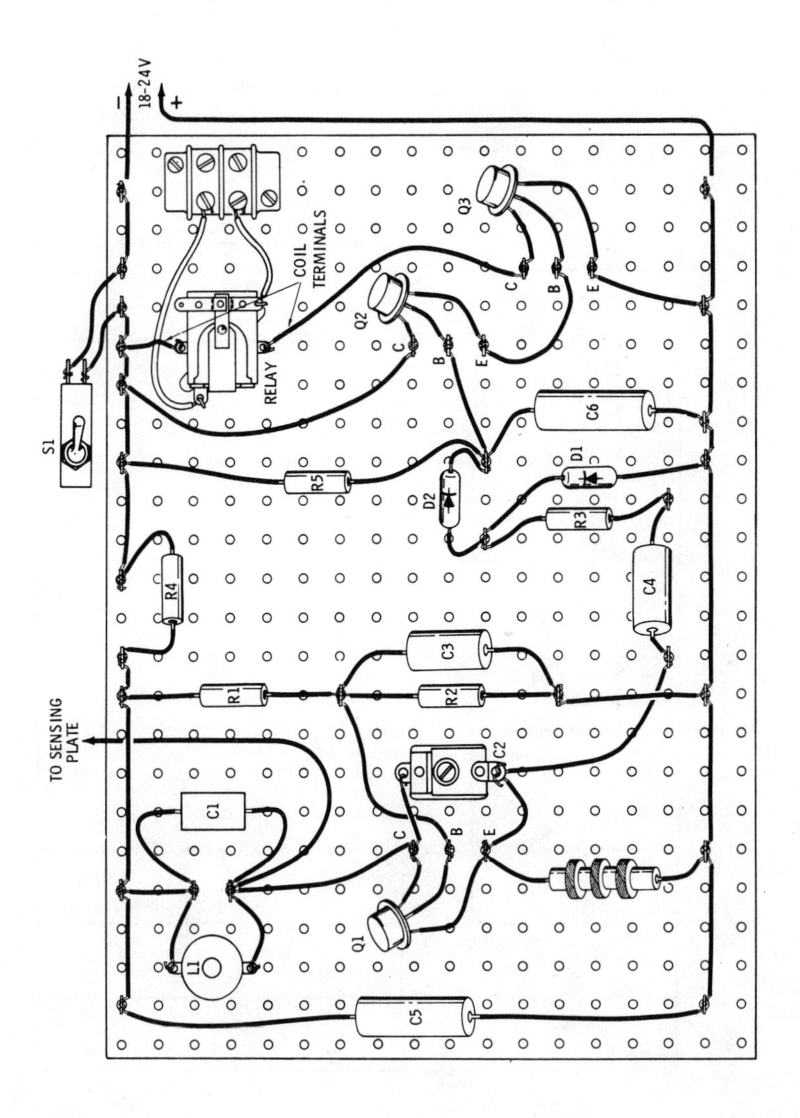

Fig. 4-6. Pictorial diagram for Fig. 4-5.

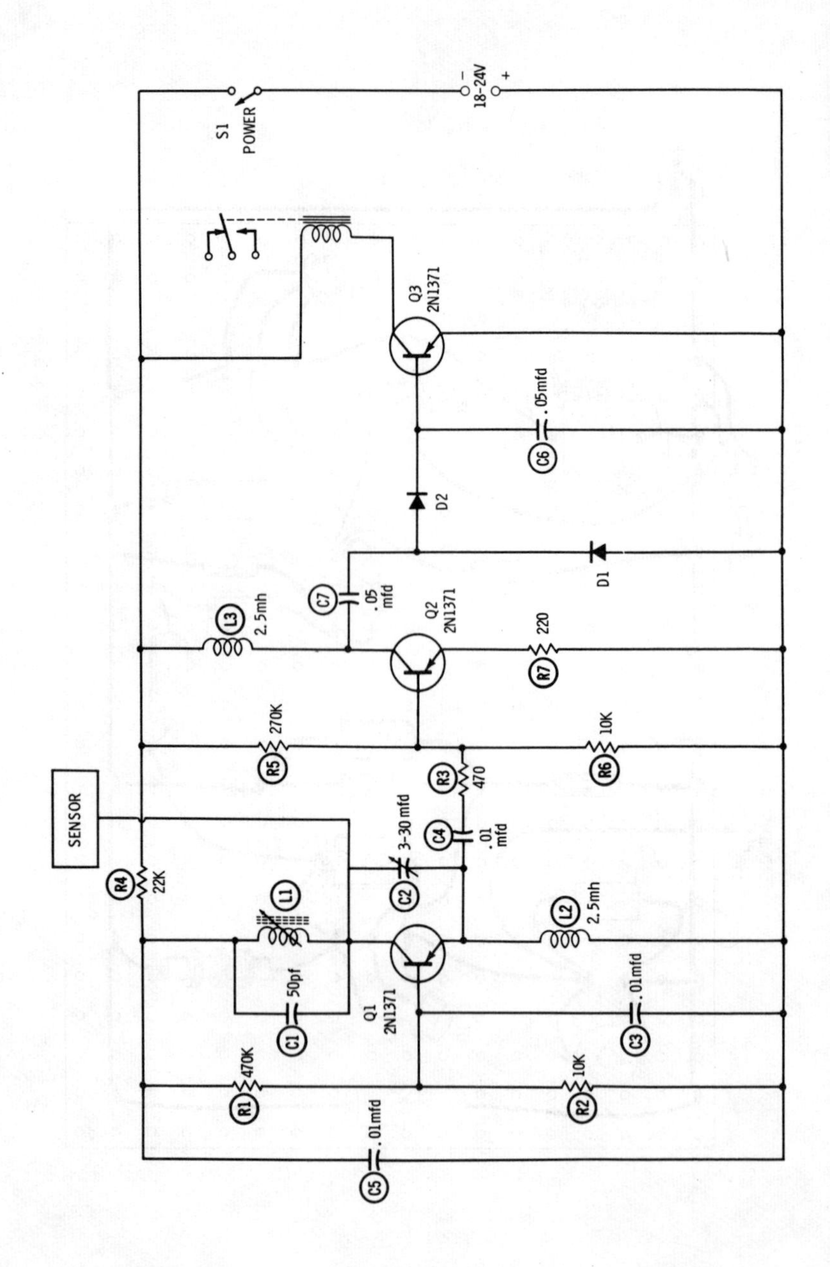

Fig. 4-7. A two-stage r-f amplifier, loaded-oscillator proximity detector.

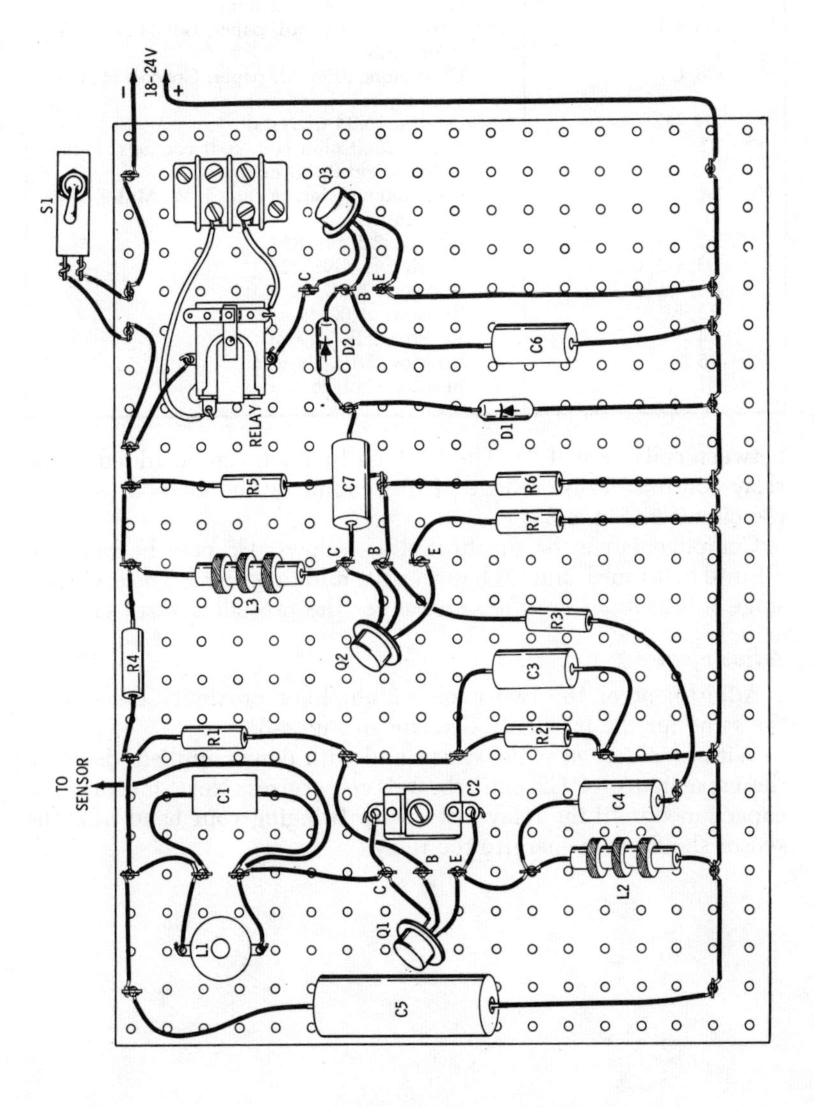

Fig. 4-8. Pictorial diagram for Fig. 4-7.

Parts List for Fig. 4-7

Item	Description
C1	Capacitor, 50 pf, mica
C2	Capacitor, 3-30 pf, trimmer
C3, C4, C5	Capacitors, .01 mfd, paper, Goodall 663UW or equiv.
C6, C7	Capacitors, .05 mfd, paper, Goodall 663UW or equiv.
D1, D2	Diodes, 1N34A, crystal
K1	Relay, 2500 ohm coil, spdt contacts, Potter Brumfield RS5D or equiv.
L1	Coil, antenna, ferrite core, J. W. Miller 4506 or equiv.
L2, L3	Chokes, 2.5 mh, RFC
Q1, Q2, Q3	Transistors, 2N1371
R1, R3	Resistors, 470K, ½ watt
R2, R6	Resistors, 10K, ½ watt
R4	Resistor, 22K, ½ watt
R5	Resistor, 270K, ½ watt
R7	Resistor, 220, ½ watt

between coils (Fig. 4-8). The latching function can be added to the relay control transistor stage of this circuit by the method used for the circuit in Fig. 4-3.

Components can be substituted as follows: C5 may be between .01 mfd to 0.1 mfd, and C6 between .01 mfd to 0.1 mfd. The oscillator stage substitutions are the same as for the preceding three circuits.

Adjustment

Adjustment of the two-stage r-f amplifier proximity detector is the same for the proximity detector in Fig. 4-3.

With no object near the sensor and with power applied, decrease the capacitance of C2 until the relay energizes. Next, increase the capacitance until the relay just opens. Bringing your hand near the sensor should now energize the relay.

Chapter 5

Elementary Metal Locators

The circuits described in this chapter are quite basic and use a maximum of three tubes or transistors. Also several nonelectronic metal locators will be discussed in this chapter. The following chapter will describe more sophisticated metal locators; several of these projects use principles not ordinarily associated with the "run of the mill' metal-locator circuits.

Most metal locators operate on one of two principles—beat frequency or loaded oscillator. The loaded-oscillator metal locator is discussed later in this chapter. In the beat-frequency metal locator, the frequency of a variable-frequency oscillator (vfo) is changed when a metallic object is in the vicinity of its tank coil. This output signal is mixed in a converter stage with a signal from a fixed-frequency oscillator. The resulting beat frequency, which varies in proportion to the difference in frequency between the two oscillators, is amplified and fed to a pair of headphones. Thus, the pitch of the signal heard in the headphones varies when a metallic object cuts into the magnetic field of the vfo tank coil.

The heterodyne function in both the beat-frequency metal locator and proximity detector is performed by identical circuits. However, the method used to shift the frequency of the variable oscillator is different in the metal locator. The frequency shift depends on the change in the inductance of the vfo tank coil rather than in the change of the capacitance as in the proximity detector. Consequently the sensor used with metal locator is a search coil instead of the sensing plate or wire of the proximity detector. Also the converter output may be amplified and applied to earphones or a speaker instead of a meter or alarm.

SINGLE-STAGE TRANSISTOR LOCATOR

Fig. 5-1 illustrates a combination of a search coil with its fixed oscillator and transistor a-m radio to form a metal locator. In this

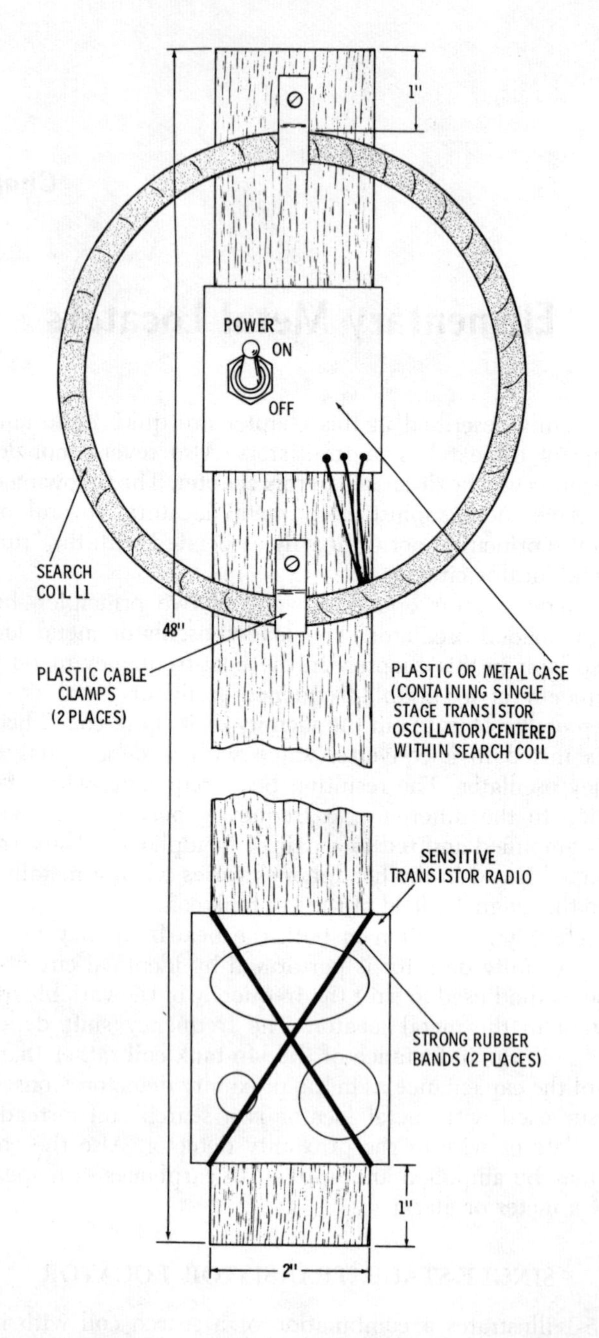

Fig. 5-1. A pictorial drawing of a single-stage transistor metal locator.

metal locator a portable a-m transistor radio functions as the fixed-frequency oscillator, and a single-transistor stage is the variable-frequency oscillator (vfo). As shown in the sketch, the transistor radio is mounted at one end of a 4-foot length of ¾-inch thick plywood, and the transistor oscillator is at the other end.

The radio is tuned to the frequency of a fairly weak station, and the frequency of the transistor vfo is adjusted to within a few hundred cycles of the station frequency. Under these conditions, a beat note (squeal) will be heard from the radio speaker. When a metallic object cuts the magnetic field of the vfo tank coil, the vfo frequency will shift. This will cause a corresponding change in the beat frequency and therefore a change in pitch of the signal heard from the radio speaker.

Fig. 5-2 is the schematic of the transistor vfo. Tank coil L1 is wound on a circular coil form. This coil is used as the search coil. The vfo circuit consists of Q1, C1, C2, C3, L1, and R1. Power is supplied by a miniature 9-volt battery.

Construction

The transistor-vfo circuit (Fig. 5-2), less the search coil, is assembled on a small piece of perforated phenolic board. Solder terminals are inserted through the phenolic board for component tie points. Wiring is shown pictorially in Fig. 5-3. The complete oscillator assembly and the 9-volt transistor battery are enclosed in a small plastic case (or metal case if better shielding is desired). The leads from search coil L1 are brought into the case through drilled holes.

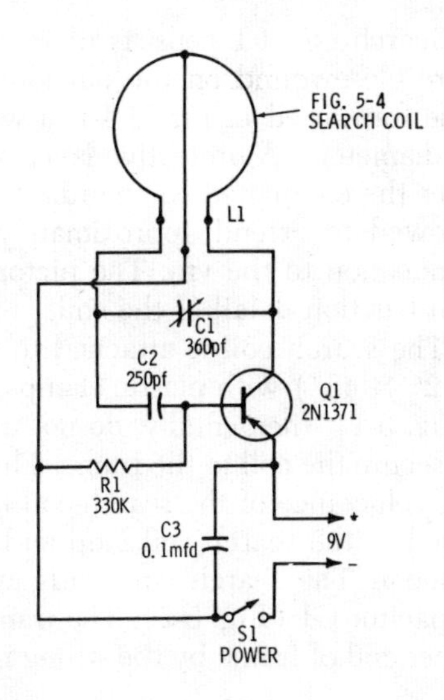

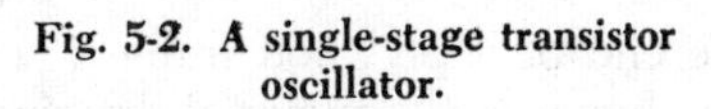
Fig. 5-2. A single-stage transistor oscillator.

Parts List for Fig. 5-2

Item	Description
C1	Capacitor, 365 pf, trimmer
C2	Capacitor, 250 pf, mica
C3	Capacitor, 0.1 mfd, paper, Goodall 663UW or equiv.
L1	Coil, search, Fig. 5-4
Q1	Transistor, 2N1371
R1	Resistor, 330K, ½ watt
S1	Switch, toggle, miniature, spst

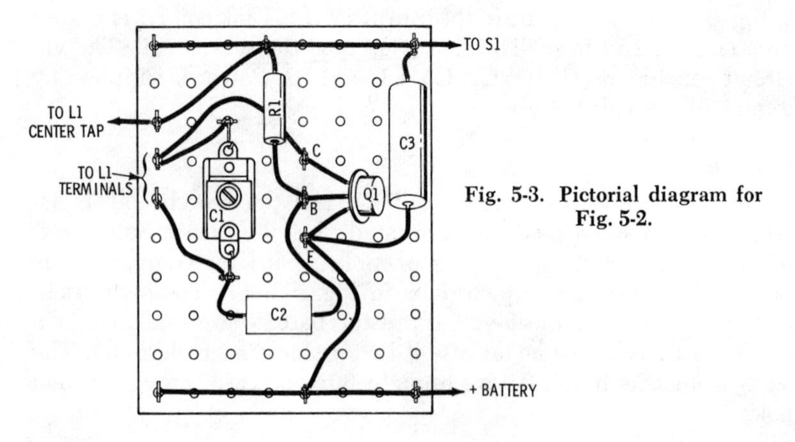

Fig. 5-3. Pictorial diagram for Fig. 5-2.

Search coil L1 consists of 20 turns on No. 22 enameled copper wire closewound on the outside perimeter of a circular coil form. The form used in Fig. 5-4 is a wooden embroidery hoop (6 inches in diameter). A protective layer of plastic electrical tape is wrapped over the completed coil windings. Both ends of the coil winding are allowed to extend approximately 4 inches from the coil form for connection to the vfo. The pictorial drawing in Fig. 5-4 shows the construction detail of the coil.

The search coil is attached to the end of a plywood frame (¾″ × 2″ × 48″) with plastic clamps, as shown in the pictorial drawing (Fig. 5-1). Incidentally, do not use metallic cable clamps or staples to secure the coil to the frame. The resulting metallic mass will affect the reluctance of the search-coil magnetic field. The vfo case is centered in the search coil loop and fastened to the frame with epoxy cement. The search coil leads are then connected across trimmer capacitor C1 (Fig. 5-2). The transistor radio can be attached to the other end of frame by the strong rubber bands illustrated in Fig. 5-1.

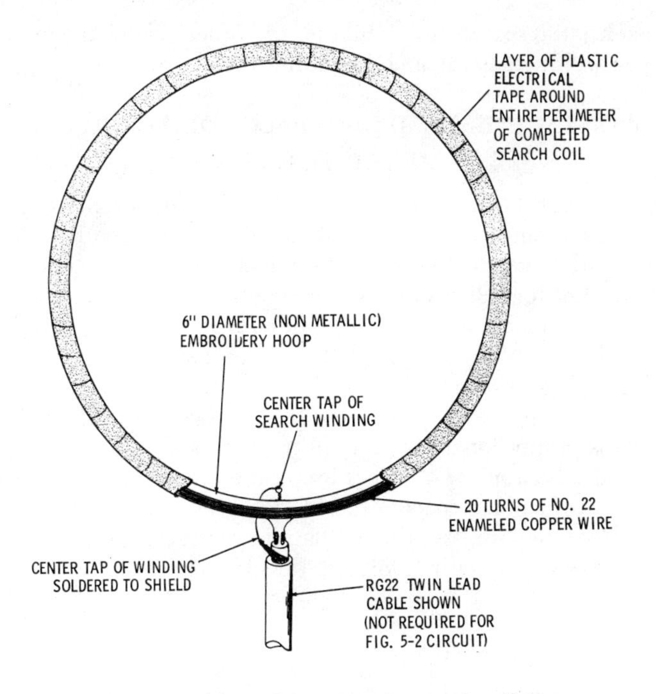

Fig. 5-4. A pictorial drawing of a search coil for metal locators.

Adjustment

After all units are assembled on the plywood strip, the metal locator is ready to be tested. Switch on the radio and turn the tuning dial of the radio until the signal of a local broadcast station is received. This station should be in the 600- to 900-kc range, preferably near the center of this range. Adjust vfo trimmer capacitor C1 until it is extended about one half of the maximum normal spacing between its plates. Turn on the power to the vfo. Adjust trimmer C1 clockwise or counterclockwise until a whistle is heard in the speaker. Continue this adjustment until the whistle stops and then restarts, set the trimmer at the point (between the two whistles) where no sound is heard from the speaker. This is the null balance point, indicating the frequencies of the vfo and radio broadcast station are equal. Bringing a metallic object, such as a pair of pliers, near the search coil should cause a change in pitch of the whistle as the frequency of vfo is changed from the null frequency (no whistle).

During adjustment of the vfo, you will notice that on one side of zero beat (when both the frequency of the vfo and the radio station are equal) the tone from the speaker will decrease as the metal object approaches the search coil, while on the other side of the zero beat, the tone will increase as metal continues to approach.

TWO-STAGE R-F AMPLIFIER LOADED-OSCILLATOR METAL LOCATOR

Fig. 5-5 is the schematic of the loaded-oscillator metal locator. The circuit is similar to the two-stage r-f amplifier loaded-oscillator proximity detector in Fig. 4-1. The major exception is that a meter is substituted for relay K1 and relay-control stage Q3.

The basic "loaded-oscillator" circuit consists of Q1, L1, C1, C2, C3, C4, L2, R1, and R2. Coil L1 is the search coil (Fig. 5-4) used for the single-stage transistor unit.

The r-f voltage developed across the voltage divider (tank L1-C1, Q1, L2) is proportional to the amplitude of oscillations developed in tank L1-C1. As a metal object is brought close to the search coil, the inductance of coil approaches the LC ratio set by the lumped capacitance across the tank and the oscillations approach maximum amplitude. A portion of the r-f voltage, developed across L2, is coupled

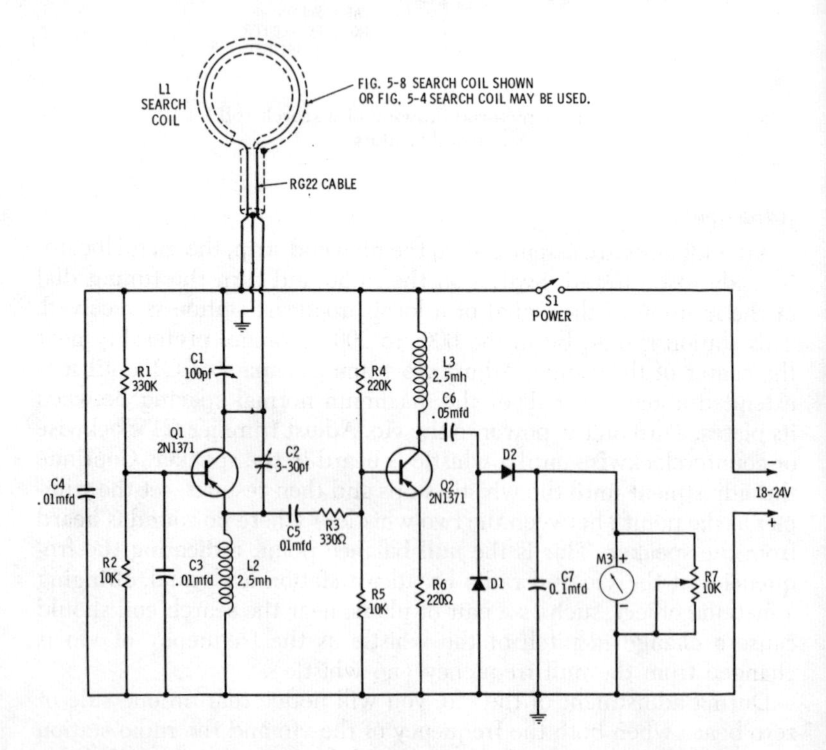

Fig. 5-5. A two-stage, r-f amplifier, loaded-oscillator metal locator.

Parts List for Fig. 5-5

Item	Description
C1	Capacitor, 100 pf, mica
C2	Capacitor, 3-30 pf, trimmer
C3, C4, C5	Capacitors, .01 mfd, paper, Goodall 663UW or equiv.
C6	Capacitor, .05 mfd, paper, Goodall 663UW or equiv.
C7	Capacitor, 0.1 mfd, paper, Goodall 663UW or equiv.
D1, D2	Diodes, 1N34A, crystal
L1	Coil, search, Fig. 5-4 or 5-8 (see text)
L2, L3	Chokes, 2.5 mh, r-f
M3	Meter, 0-50 microammeter
Q1, Q2	Transistors, 2N1371
R1, R3	Resistors, 330K, ½ watt
R2, R5	Resistors, 10K, ½ watt
R4, R6	Resistors, 220K, ½ watt
R7	Potentiometer, 10K, 1 watt, linear taper

to the r-f amplifier stage via C5 and R3. The r-f amplifier stage (Q2, R4, R5, R6, and L3) amplifies the signal and applies it to the voltage-doubler rectifier (D1, D2, C6, and C7). The output of this rectifier is fed to meter M3. Potentiometer R7 is shunted across the meter and controls its range. With no metallic object cutting the magnetic field of the search coil, feedback capacitor C2 is adjusted for maximum indication on the meter. Now, the r-f oscillations in the tank and consequently the voltage at the emitter of Q1 are at maximum values. This voltage is amplified by the second stage (Q2), rectified by the voltage-doubler stage, and applied across meter M3. When an object approaches the search coil, the amplitude of the oscillations of tank L1-C1 is reduced, and a lower output voltage is developed at the emitter of Q1. The reduced emitter voltage is reflected in the meter as a lower indication.

Construction

The loaded-oscillator metal locator is assembled on a piece of perforated phenolic board. The layout of components is not critical, except that L2 and L3 must be well separated from each other to avoid intercoupling as shown in the pictorial diagram of Fig. 5-6.

The search coil (L1) is wound on a wooden coil form (embroidery hoop), and the finished coil is covered with electrical tape for physical protection. Fig. 5-4 shows the details for the search-coil construction.

The completed search coil (Fig. 5-4) is fastened to the bottom of the plywood base of the two-stage metal locator of Fig. 5-7. The

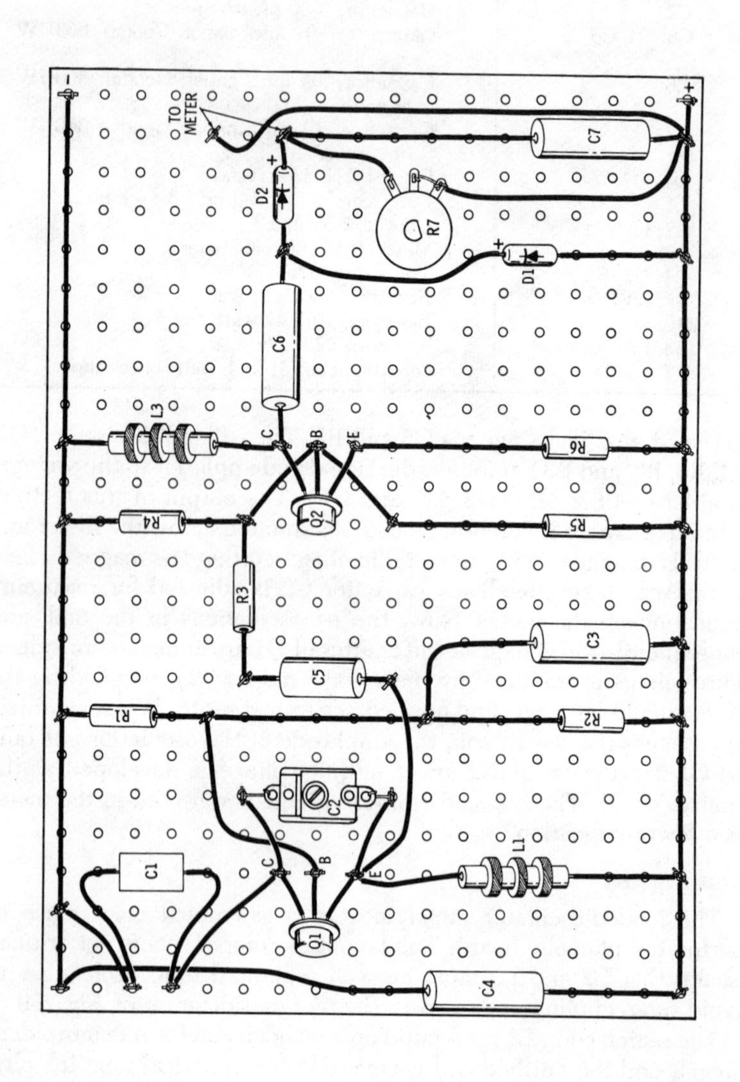

Fig. 5-6. Pictorial diagram for Fig. 5-5.

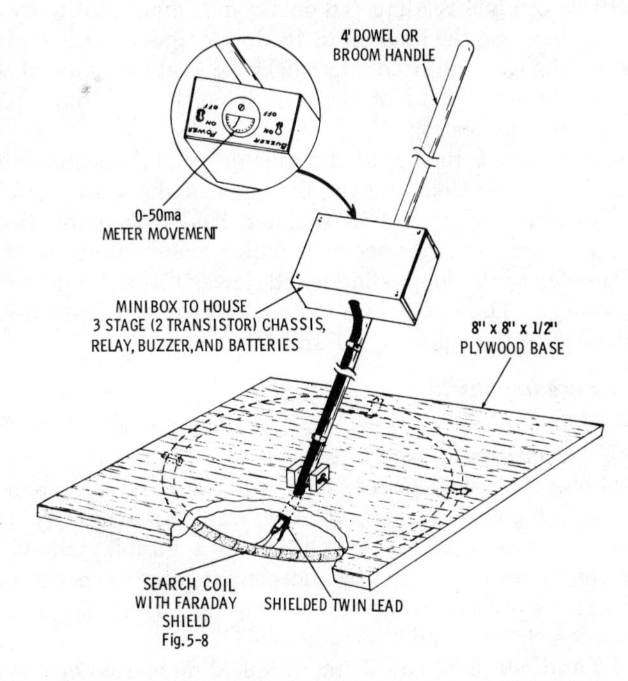

Fig. 5-7. A pictorial drawing of a two-stage metal locator.

wood dowel or broom handle is fastened onto the opposite side of the base to serve as a handle. The wired chassis (Fig. 5-6) is assembled into the minibox. Assemble the power switch and meter into the box. Secure completed box assembly halfway up the handle.

Component substitutions are as follows: R1 may range from 330K to 680K, R2 (10K to 15K), R3 (330 to 560 ohms, R6 (220 to 330 ohms), C2 (.02 mfd to .1 mfd), C5 (.01 mfd to .1 mfd), C6 (.01 mfd to .1 mfd), and C7 (.1 mfd to .5 mfd).

Adjustment

When the unit is completed and thoroughly checked for wiring errors, it is ready for testing. Set sensitivity control R7 at maximum resistance, and turn on the battery switch. Turn the adjusting screw of trimmer C2 clockwise until maximum indication is attained. If the meter goes off scale as the trimmer screw is turned clockwise, adjust R7 to bring the meter pointer back to approximately one half of full scale. When maximum indication is obtained on the meter, the metal-locator oscillator is set for maximum amplitude of oscillations.

When a piece of ferrous material (any iron or steel object) cuts the magnetic field of the search coil, the meter should dip to about one-fourth its original reading. To obtain maximum sensitivity from this circuit, decrease the amount of feedback signal in the oscillator stage by turning C2 slightly counterclockwise (without a metal object cutting the magnetic field of the search coil) and adjust R7 for maximum meter indication.

The sensitivity of the "loaded-oscillator" metal locator can be further increased by enlarging the diameter of the search-coil loop. This will increase the size of its radiated field. When this is done, however, it is necessary to experiment with a lower value of C1. Also, as the diameter of the loop is increased, fewer turns should be used on its perimeter. The circuit itself is not critical and will tolerate a wide variation in the values of L1 and C1.

Adding a Faraday Shield

In the preceding two circuits, the search coil responds to "hand capacity" (electrostatic field) as well as the metallic (electromagnetic) objects. This "hand capacity" will cause the meter to deflect when the search coil is touched. To avoid this "hand-capacity" effect, it is necessary to encase the search coil in a Faraday shield. The Faraday shield prevents electrostatic coupling between the search coil and nearby objects, while still permitting electromagnetic coupling between the coil and a metallic object.

Figs. 5-8 and 5-9 show how Faraday shielding is used on the completed search coil of Fig. 5-4. A layer of No. 20 or No. 22 enameled wire is wound spirally over the taped search-coil winding of Fig. 5-4. The spacing between is approximately the thickness of a single wire.

Notice that the winding does not go completely around the perimeter of the search coil—a gap (½ inch wide) being left between the start and finish of the winding. This gap prevents the Faraday shield winding from becoming a shorted turn and short-circuiting the magnetic field generated in the search coil.

When the Faraday shield is completed, one end of the shield wire is connected to chassis ground. A slight additional capacitance is added to tank L1-C1 by the Faraday shield and will cause a small change in the oscillator frequency. Capacitor C1 is adjusted to compensate for this capacitance.

The beat-frequency and loaded-oscillator metal locator circuits described so far are capable of sensing both ferrous and nonferrous metallic objects *when the search coil is not shielded.* However, the sensitivity is much greater when sensing ferrous objects.

Adding a Relay

Should you get weary of constantly keeping an eye on the meter of the metal locator, you can add a relay to actuate a bell. The circuit in Fig. 5-5 can be modified by removing meter M3 and substituting

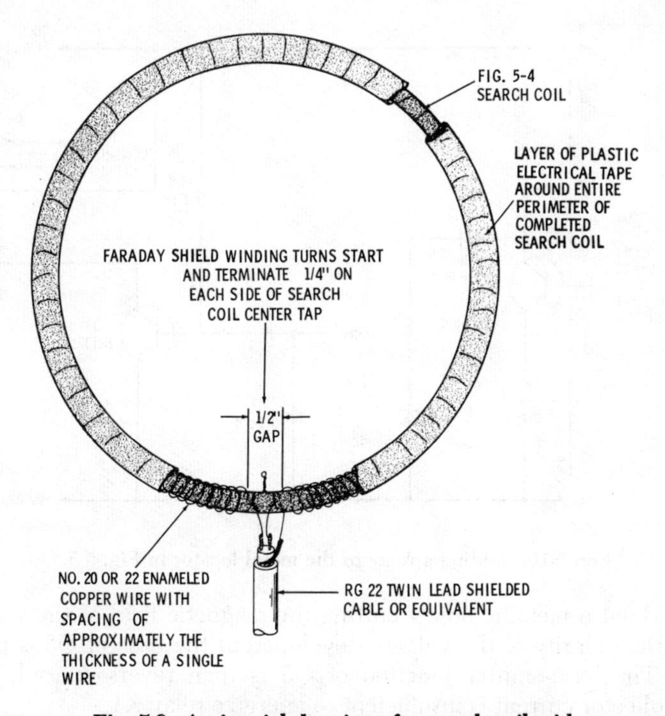

Fig. 5-8. A pictorial drawing of a search coil with a Faraday shield.

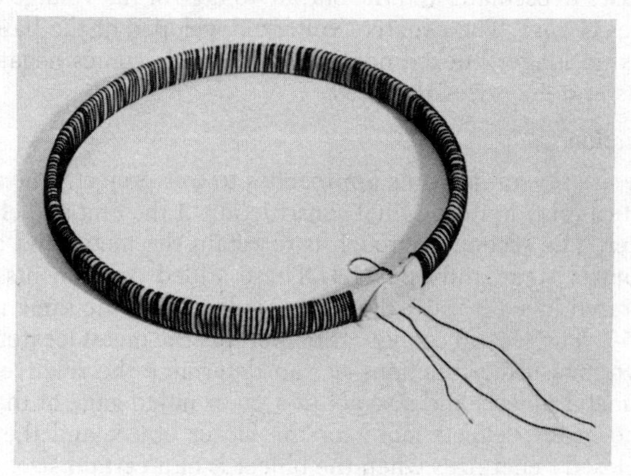

Fig. 5-9. A search coil with a Faraday shield.

transistor Q3 and relay K1 as shown in Fig. 5-10 and 5-11. With this modification, the circuit is essentially the same as the proximity-detector circuit (Fig. 4-7) described in Chapter 4.

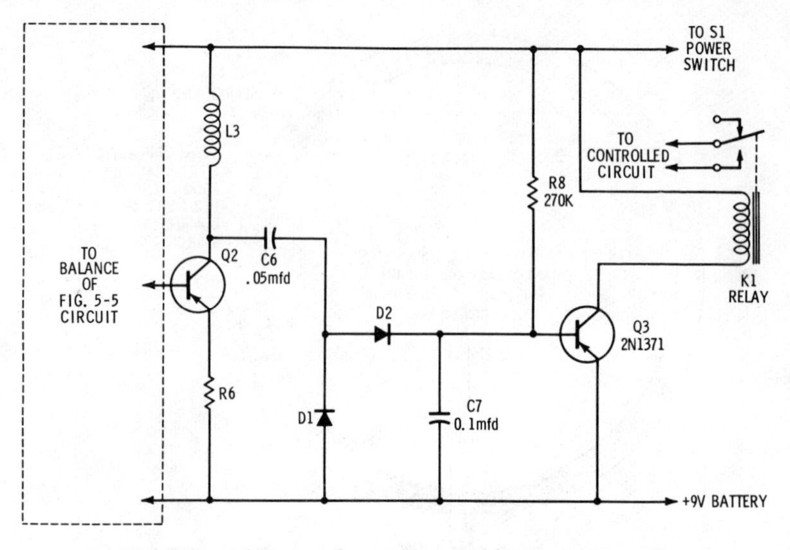

Fig. 5-10. Adding a relay to the metal locator in Fig. 5-5.

Without a metallic object cutting the magnetic field of the search coil, the polarity of the voltage developed at the base of Q3 is positive. The base-emitter junction of Q3 is then reverse-biased, and the collector current is insufficient to energize relay K1.

When a ferrous metallic object cuts the search-coil field, the oscillator ceases to oscillate, and the output voltage of the voltage doubler decreases to zero. The negative voltage developed at the base of Q3 by R8 is no longer bucked out, and the base becomes negative. Q3 conducts and energizes the relay.

Construction

There are several possible approaches to this project. One is to incorporate a relay in the original construction of the unit and eliminate the meter. The second approach is to retain the meter and add the relay control stage and relay K1. These added components can be incorporated in a separate, plug-in module or into the same minibox of Fig. 5-7. The second configuration permits the metal locator to perform two measuring functions—it can determine the relative size of several metal objects and also act as a go or no-go gage of the object size. The meter deflects more for the larger object and the buzzer (relay closed) energizes when the object is of a certain size.

Adjustment

The feedback capacitor (C2) is adjusted so that relay K1 remains de-energized without a metal object near the sensing plate. The relay (K1) now should energize when a piece of ferrous metal cuts

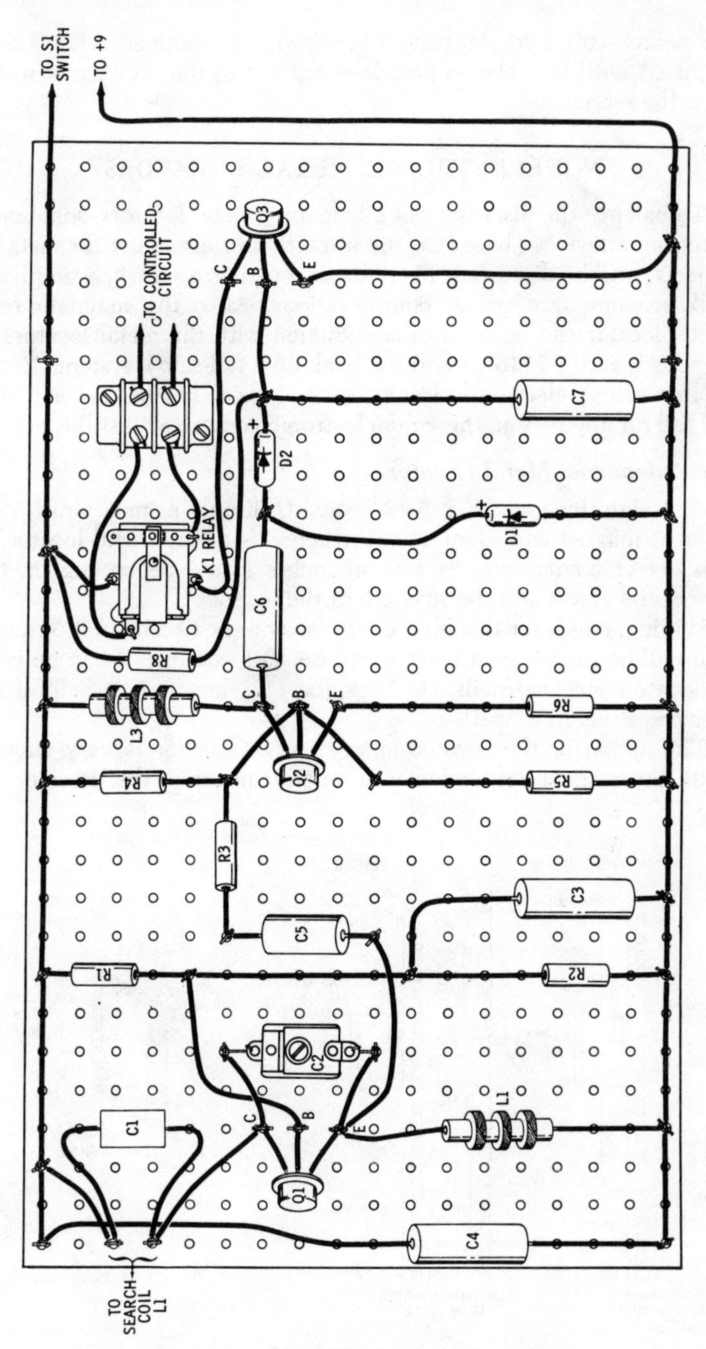

Fig. 5-11. Pictorial diagram of Fig. 5-10.

the search-coil field. Maximum sensitivity is obtained when C2 is adjusted until the relay is just de-energized in the absence of metal near the search coil.

NONELECTRONIC METAL LOCATORS

To balance the discussion of elementary metal locators, some nonelectronic devices (based on the attraction of a magnet for metallic objects) will be discussed. These devices can be used when simplicity and economy are prime considerations. Also, the magnetic-reed metal locator can be used in conjunction with the metal locators in Figs. 5-1 and 5-7, to provide a back-up (fail-safe) system. If the more sensitive electronic circuits, such as those in Figs. 5-1 and Fig. 5-7 fail for any reason, these nonelectronic controls will still function.

Pivoted-magnet Metal Locator

Although this unit (Fig. 5-12) consists of only a small alnico permanent magnet and pivot, it nevertheless is a true metal locator. It can detect ferrous objects several inches away, depending on the size of the object and the strength of the magnet.

While the uses for this little gadget may at first seem a bit obscure, you will be surprised at what it can do. For example, it can be used to locate concealed nails, steel staples, etc.; hence, it is helpful for locating studs in a wall.

The action of the pivoted-magnet metal locator is very simple. With the magnet suspended in a vertical position, the detector as-

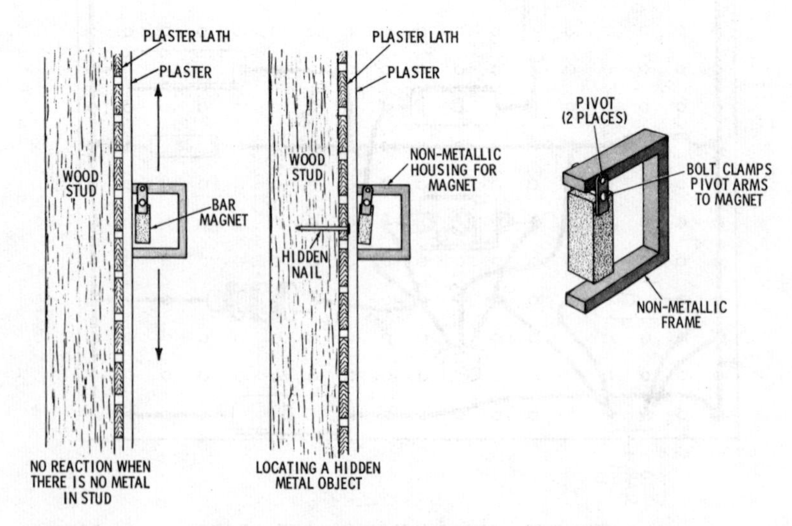

Fig. 5-12. A pivoted-magnet metal locator.

sembly is slowly moved over the surface to be checked as shown in Fig. 5-12. If a piece of ferrous metal (nail, screw, etc.) approaches the magnet, the magnet will move toward the metallic object as shown in Fig. 5-12.

The construction of the pivoted-magnet metal locator is self-explanatory. If the magnet is to respond to small changes in its magnetic path, a powerful magnet must be used. A horseshoe magnet can be substituted for the bar magnet; however, the pole pieces should face toward the wall or any other surface being checked.

Magnetic-Reed Metal Locator

Although the magnetic field is not changed as in a true metallic locator, the magnetic field can be interrupted to open a switch controlled by a magnetic field. The opened switch will indicate that a metallic object is between the switch and magnet.

Fig. 5-13 illustrates the basic construction and operation of a magnetically actuated switch. The switch itself consists of a glass tube in which are contained two contact blades arranged so that the two switch contacts are separated in the absence of a magnetic field. When approached by a magnetic field, the contacts close with a snap action, and remain closed until the magnetic field is removed.

Electrically, the magnetic-reed switch specified here can be considered an spst normally-open switch. A solid lead is brought out of each end of the glass tube for connection to the circuit. Fig. 5-13 is a demonstration of magnetic-reed switch action.

The sensitivity of the switch in Fig. 5-14 will range from about ¼ inch when actuated by a ¾ x ⅛ inch alnico bar magnet to better

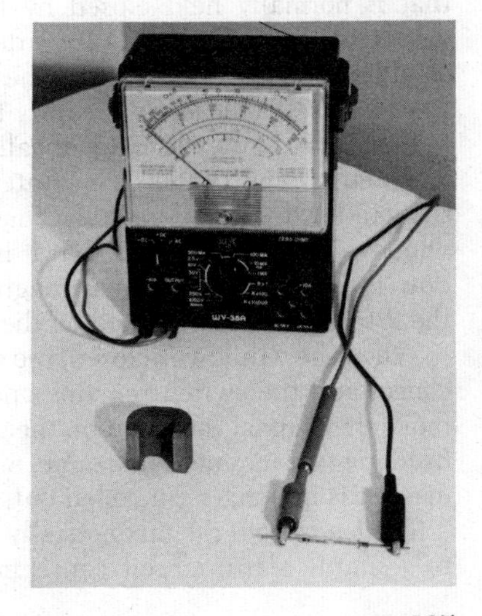

Fig. 5-13. A demonstration of magnetic-reed switch action.

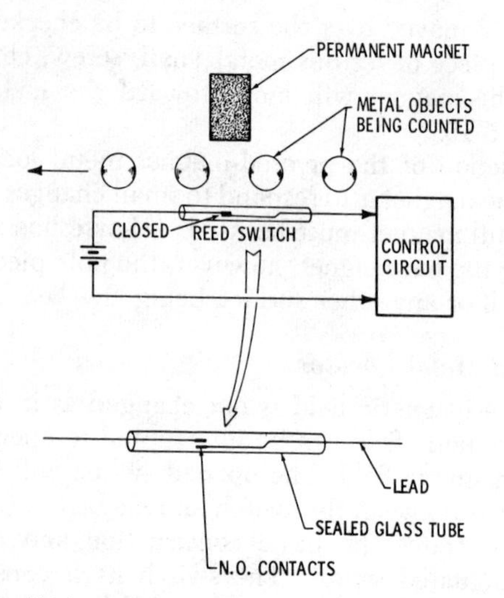

Fig. 5-14. A magnetic-reed switch metal counter.

than 1 to 1½ inches when actuated by a 1½ inch diameter alnico horseshoe magnet. The actuating distance varies directly with the magnetic field. This switch (G. E. type 2DR50 or equivalent) is also called a dry-reed switch.

Fig. 5-14 shows the switch in an arrangement to detect hidden ferrous metal objects. The switch and magnet are placed on opposite sides of the material to be checked. A piece of ferrous metal passing between the magnet and switch will act as a magnetic shield, and prevents the magnetic field from reaching the switch. The switch that is normally held closed by the magnetic field will open and actuate a control circuit. In order to provide sufficient magnetic shielding area to de-energize the switch, the metallic object must have an area at least as great as the face of the actuating magnet.

Fig. 5-15 shows the magnetically actuated switch used as a burglar alarm. The switch is mounted on a small bracket fastened to the window frame. A small bar magnet is mounted on the sash of the window in such a manner that it is facing the switch when the window is closed. A second bar magnet, oriented to cancel the field of the first magnet, is mounted on the window frame next to the switch.

When the window is closed, the opposing fields of the two magnets cancel and the switch remains open. Raising the window sash will move the magnet mounted on the sash away from the switch and the fixed magnet mounted on frame. Since the magnetic field of the fixed magnet is no longer cancelled out, its field will close the switch.

The leads from the magnetically operated switch can be connected to a simple alarm circuit consisting of a power source (battery or

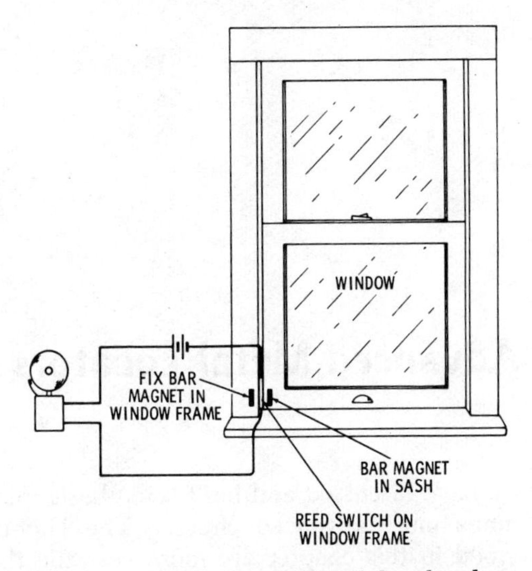

Fig. 5-15. A magnetic-reed switch burglar alarm.

bell transformer) and a buzzer. A big advantage of this setup is that no power is consumed during standby periods when the switch is not closed.

Chapter 6

Advanced Metal Locators

Now that we have discussed and built some basic metal locators, we will try some more advanced circuits. The Hall-effect metal locators described in this chapter are more versatile than any circuits discussed in Chapter 5. There are many applications which will become apparent as you experiment with the following circuits.

PRINCIPLES OF THE HALL EFFECT

Any charged particle (electron or hole) moving through a magnetic field experiences a force that is perpendicular both to its direction motion and the the direction of an applied magnetic field. This force pushes the electrons toward one edge, where they tend to accumulate.

The Hall effect is similar to the deflection of electrons in the picture tube of a television receiver. In the picture tube the electrons are deflected by an electromagnetic force developed by the vertical deflection coils around the neck of the tube.

This principle is used in the Hall generator. The generator is a thin wafer (element) of semiconductor material (a typical material is indium arsenide) and is encapsulated in sintered ceramic and cast resin for strength. The photos in Figs. 6-1 and 6-2 illustrate the size and types of Hall-generator configurations.

The wafer, or element, is small in size and rectangular in shape. Typical dimensions of a wafer are 0.1 mm × 2 mm × 4 mm. The average output of the element is about 10 millivolts per kilogauss. As shown in Fig. 6-3 when a voltage (either ac or dc) is applied across the longitudinal ends of the wafer with a magnetic field applied at right angles to the wafer (length and width) a control current will flow through the length of the element. The flow of charges (electrons or holes) in this control current will accumulate at the ohmic contacts on the element, and a voltage will be indicated on the meter.

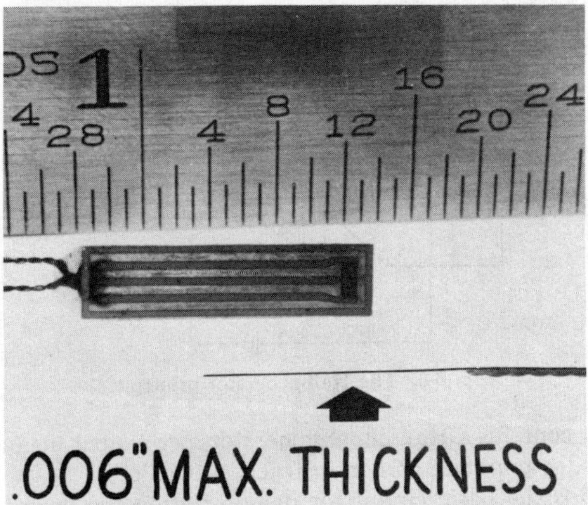

Fig. 6-1. The physical size of Hall-effect generators.

Since the voltage developed by the Hall generator is very low (in the millivolt range), it must be amplified for use in a metal-locator circuit. A d-c amplifier is used to increase the output voltage of the Hall generator when a d-c current is used in the generator—an a-c amplifier is used when an a-c control curent is fed to the generator.

THE BASIC HALL-GENERATOR CIRCUIT

Hall effect generators are available from a number of sources. Complete Hall-effect experimenter's kits are available. A typical kit

Fig. 6-2. The various types of Hall-generator packaging.

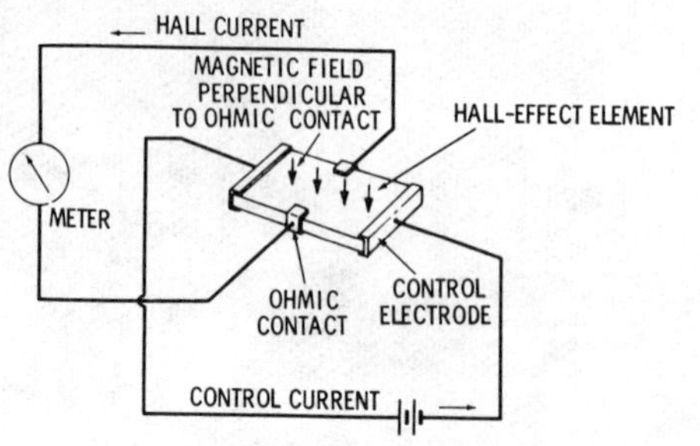

Fig. 6-3. The Hall-generator principle.

(Fig. 6-4) contains a Hall-effect generator, permanent magnet, transistorized d-c amplifier, and an instruction booklet.

Fig. 6-5 is the basic circuit for demonstrating the operation of a Hall-effect generator. The Hall generator is an Ohio Semiconductor Type HR-33 or its equivalent. The HR-33 generator has four leads, two of these leads (black and green) connect to the source of control current, and the other two leads (red and blue) deliver the generated voltage. A 33-ohm resistor (R1) limits the current through the Hall generator to its rated value.

The output leads from the generator can be connected to a 0-50-microampere meter to indicate the presence of the voltage. With everything set up, apply power and bring a permanent magnet near the Hall generator. The meter will indicate when a voltage is developed in the generator. The Hall voltage will change with a change in the distance between the magnet and generator.

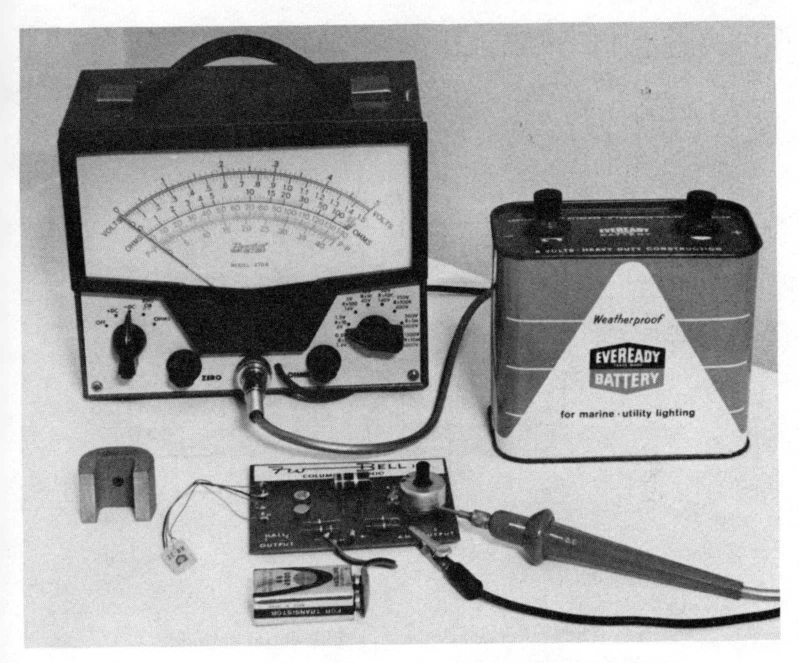

Fig. 6-4. A typical Hall-effect experimenter kit.

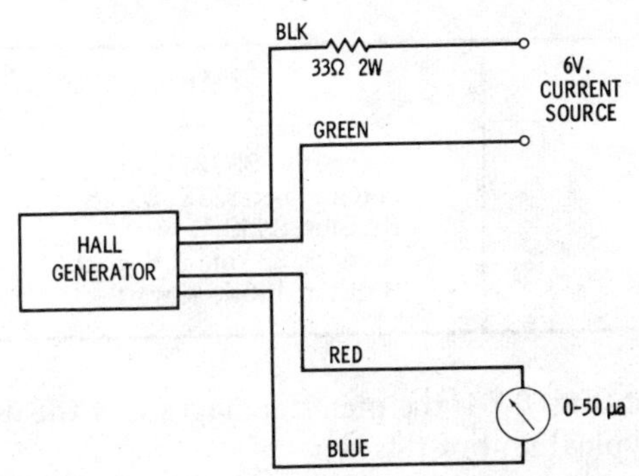

Fig. 6-5. A basic Hall-generator circuit.

A HALL GENERATOR WITH DIFFERENTIAL AMPLIFIER

While the preceding setup (Fig. 6-5) is useful for demonstrating the basic Hall effect, the sensitivity of this circuit is insufficient. Fig. 6-6 is the schematic of a simple transistorized differential amplifier that will increase the output of the Hall generator. Q1, Q2, R1, R2, R3, R4, R5, R6 and R7 form the basic circuit. A 500 microammeter connected from collector to collector of Q1 and Q2 will indicate the

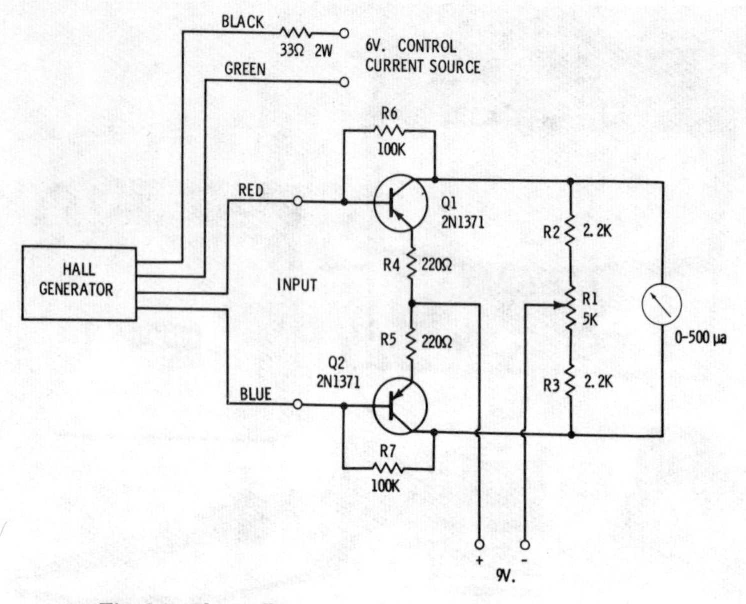

Fig. 6-6. The Hall generator with a differential amplifier.

Parts List for Fig. 6-6

Item	Description
Q1, Q2	Transistor, 2N1371
R1	Potentiometer, 5K, 2 watt
R2, R3	Resistor, 2.2K, ½ watt
R4, R5	Resistor, 220 ohm, ½ watt
R6, R7	Resistor, 100K, ½ watt

output current. Fig. 6-7 is the pictorial diagram of the amplifier. Fig. 6-8 shows a typical unit of this type.

Apply battery power to the Hall genator and the differential amplifier. With the generator removed from any magnetic fields, the balance control (R1) is adjusted to obtain a zero meter reading. Bringing a permanent magnet near the Hall-effect element will give an indication on the meter.

In working with the Hall generator, it will be noted that the polarity of the Hall output voltage depends on the direction of the flux path of the applied magnetic field. It is possible to determine whether the north or south pole of a magnet is being presented to the Hall generator by noting the polarity of the Hall voltage.

An a-c Hall voltage can also be obtained from the Hall generator by substituting a 6.3-volt filament transformer for the 6-volt current source indicated in Fig. 6-6. This transformer should have a secondary-winding current rating of at least 0.5 ampere. When supplying the Hall generator with a-c control current, either an oscilloscope or an a-c vtvm can be connected to the output of the differential amplifier to indicate the Hall voltage.

With an a-c powered Hall generator, the residual Hall voltage can be nulled out by biasing the generator with a permanent magnet. Simply place the magnet near the Hall generator until the minimum Hall voltage is obtained without an additional magnetic field in the

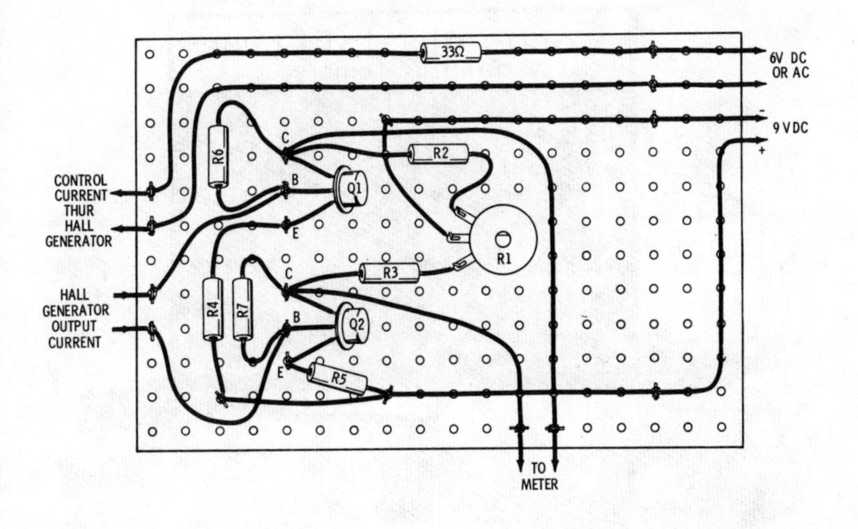

Fig. 6-7. Pictorial diagram of Fig. 6-6 amplifier.

vicinity of the generator. When the residual Hall voltage is nulled out, the circuit will be extremely sensitive to a magnetic field change.

A HALL-GENERATOR METAL LOCATOR

Fig. 6-9 shows how the Hall generator can be used as a metal detector. The generator is connected to an isolated 6.3-volt a-c source, and its output signal is fed to a high-gain audio amplifier. The generator is biased with a small permanent magnet to obtain zero indication on the meter without another external magnetic field or a ferrous object in the immediate vicinity.

When a ferrous object is placed close to the Hall generator, the lines of force of the bias magnet are "distorted." This "distortion" of the magnetic field alters the biasing characteristics of the magnet, and a Hall output voltage is developed.

The voltage from the amplifier can be applied to an a-c volt-meter to indicate the amplitude of the Hall voltage, or rectified and applied to a relay control stage similar to the final stage of Fig. 4-1.

The one advantage of this type of metal detector over the units described in Chapter 5 is the concentrated area scanned by the Hall-effect element. Because only a small area is scanned, this unit permits the individual detection of closely-spaced metallic objects.

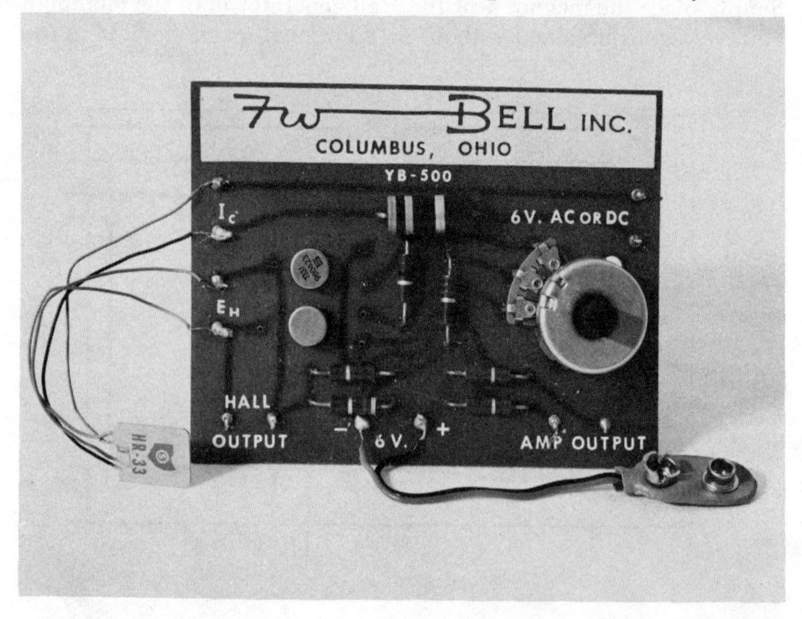

Courtesy F. W. Bell Inc.

Fig. 6-8. A typical Hall-effect differential amplifier.

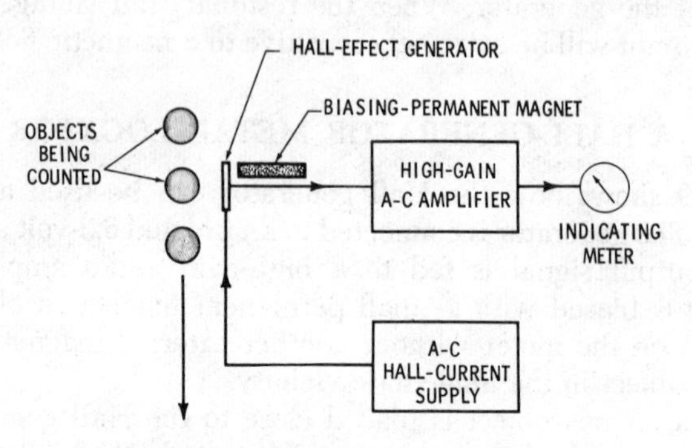

Fig. 6-9. The Hall-generator metal locator.

CHANGING-FIELD METAL LOCATOR

Fig. 6-10 is the schematic of a metal locator that will respond only to moving ferrous-metallic objects. This type of locator is not sensitive to stationary metal and thus will not respond to other nearby stationary metallic objects.

In operation, when a ferrous metallic object passes by sensing coil L1, a current pulse is generated in the coil due to the disturbance of the magnetic field produced by the magnetic core of the coil.

The current pulse is applied to the control grid of V1A. The amplified pulse developed at the plate of V1A is applied to V1B where it is further amplified. The pulse appearing at the plate of V1B is applied to the control grid of V2 and drives the control grid of V2 positive with respect to its cathode. V2 will fire and energize the relay.

The power supply is a conventional circuit, consisting of T1, CR1, C5, C6, R10, and R11.

Construction

The "changing-field" metal counter can be assembled on a small aluminum chassis. Parts layout is not critical, except that direct leads must be used in the input section of the amplifier–V1A and its associated components. The pictorial diagram of Fig. 6-11 shows this arrangement.

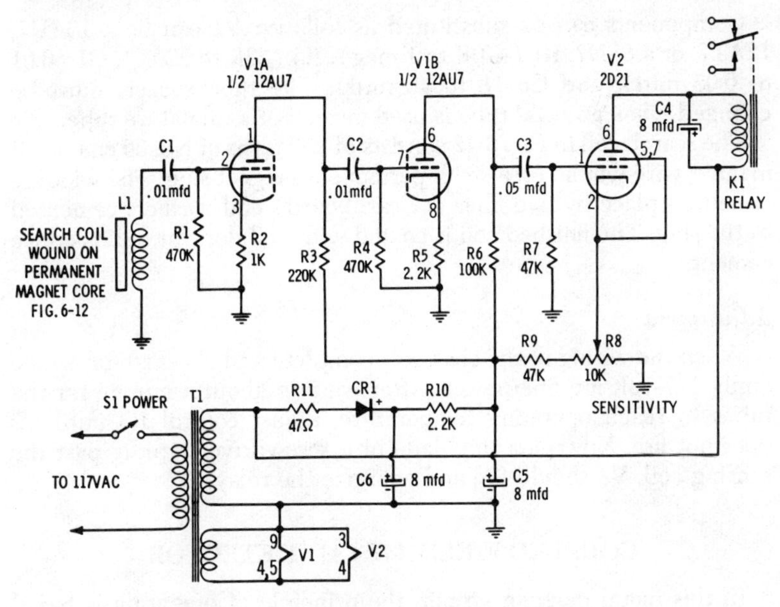

Fig. 6-10. A changing-field metal locator.

Parts List for Fig. 6-10

Item	Description
C1, C2	Capacitor, .01 mfd, paper, Goodall 663UW or equiv.
C3	Capacitor, .05 mfd, paper, Goodall 663UW or equiv.
C4, C5, C6	Capacitors, 8mfd, 150v, electrolytic
CR1	Rectifier, silicon, 1N2484 or equiv.
K1	Relay, 5000 ohm d-c coil, spdt contacts, Potter Brumfield RS5D or equiv.
L1	Coil, search. Fig. 6-10
R7, R9	Resistors, 47K, ½ watt, carbon
R2	Resistor, 1K, ½ watt, carbon
R3	Resistor, 220K, ½ watt, carbon
R1, R4	Resistors, 470K, ½ watt, carbon
R5, R10	Resistors, 2.2K, ½ watt, carbon
R6	Resistor, 100K, ½ watt, carbon
R8	Resistor, 10K, ½ watt, carbon
R11	Resistor, 47, ½ watt, carbon
S1	Switch, toggle, spdt
T1	Transformer, power, pri. 117v, sec. 125v @ 50 ma, 6.3v @ 2 amp
V1	Tube, 12AU7
V2	Tube, 2D21

Components can be substituted as follows: V1 can be a 12AU7, 12AT7, or a 6SN7, R1 (470K to 1 meg), R3 (33K to 220K), C1 (0.01 to 0.05 mfd), and C6 (8 to 40 mfd). The tube sockets must be changed when an octal tube is used instead of a miniature tube.

The search coil in Fig. 6-12 consists of 250 turns of No. 30 enameled magnet wire wound on a small permanent magnet slug. The winding is held in place by two fiber (or cardboard) end washers cemented to the slug. The finished coil is coated with coil dope or radio service cement.

Adjustment

When the wiring of the chassis is complete and checked for errors, apply 117-volt a-c line power. After waiting about a minute for the tubes to reach operating temperature, adjust control R8 until V2 does not fire. Now pass the blade of a screwdriver rapidly past the sensing coil. V2 should fire and energize the relay.

COUPLED-FIELD METAL DETECTOR

In this metal detector circuit, the principle of operation is based on the coupling of a magnetic field from a transmitting coil to a

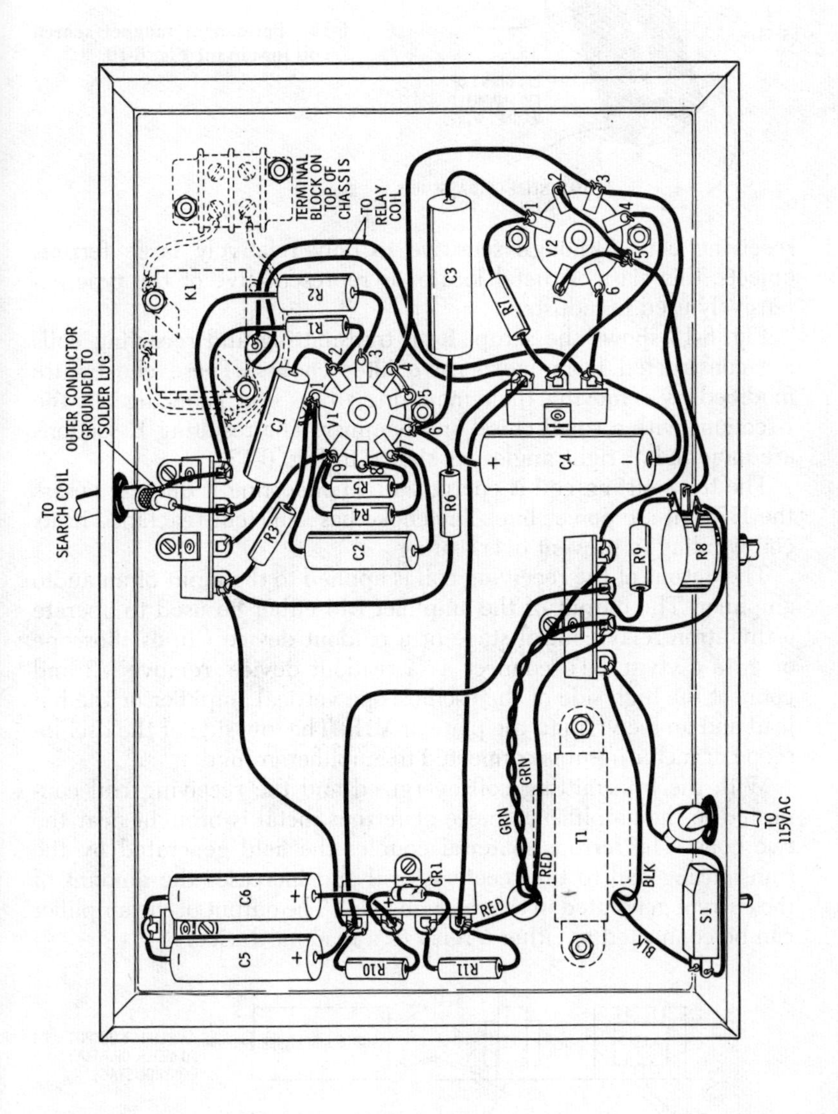

Fig. 6-11. Pictorial diagram for Fig. 6-10.

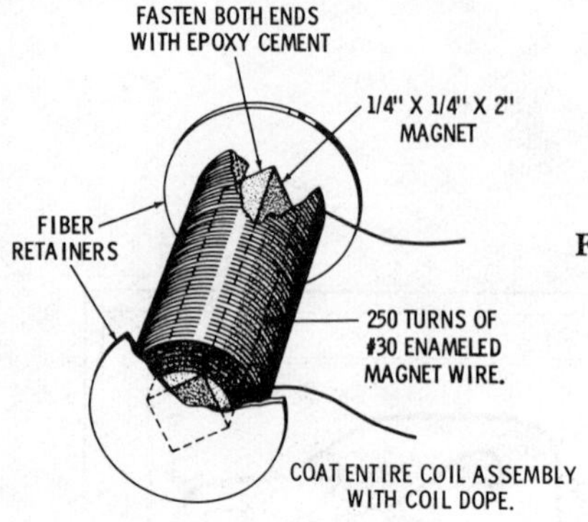

Fig. 6-12. Permanent magnet search coil for circuit Fig. 6-10.

receiving coil. Although sensitive to only relatively large ferrous objects, this class of metal locator is representative of the type extensively used in industry.

Fig. 6-13 shows the setup. Both transmitting and receiving coils are constructed from inexpensive filter chokes. These chokes are modified by removing their mounting straps and knocking out the I-sections with a small chisel and hammer. The resulting E sections are mounted at right angles, as shown in Fig. 6-13.

The transmitting coil is energized by connecting it directly across the 117-volt a-c power line. The choke has sufficient reactance in its coil winding to prevent overheating.

The output of the receiving coil is applied to the input of an audio amplifier. The output of the amplifier can either be used to operate a thyratron relay control stage or a readout device (an oscilloscope or an a-c vtvm). To connect as a readout device, remove V2 and connect the high side of the oscilloscope vertical amplifier or the hot lead and an a-c vtvm to the plate of V1B. The low side of the oscilloscope or meter input is connected to amplifier ground.

With the transmitting coil energized and the receiving coil connected to the amplifier, a piece of ferrous metal is brought near the two coils. The ferrous material couples the field generated by the transmitting coil to the receiving coil and increases the amount of the current generated in the receiving coil. The output of the amplifier can be connected to either a relay or a readout device.

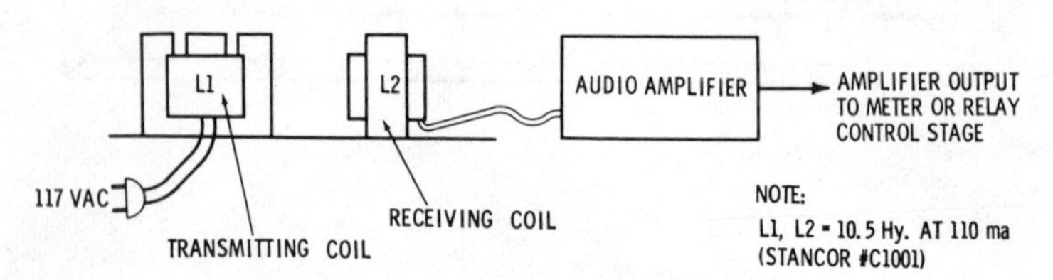

Fig. 6-13. A coupled-field metal locator.

AN "OFF-RESONANCE" METAL LOCATOR

This is a metal-locator circuit that operates on the principle of the change in the inductance of a search coil in a resonant r-f tank circuit. A constant-amplitude and constant-frequency oscillator supplies r-f energy to this search-coil tank. In previous metal-locator circuits, a change in search coil inductance was used to vary either the amplitude or frequency of an oscillator.

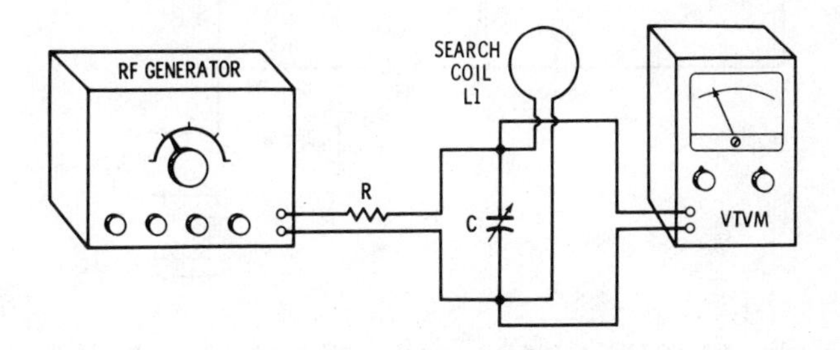

Fig. 6-14. The off-resonance metal locator.

Fig. 6-14 shows the basic principles of the "off-resonance" metal locator. The parallel-resonant LC circuit is connected to the output of an r-f signal generator with an isolating resistor in the "hot" lead.

The signal generator is tuned to the resonant frequency of the parallel-resonant circuit. The r-f voltage developed across the resonant circuit is at a maximum value. The vtvm (switched to its a-c scale) reads the r-f voltage developed across the LC circuit.

When a metallic object nears the resonant circuit, the inductance of L is changed and the LC circuit is detuned. Since the resonant frequency of the LC circuit is now different from the signal produced by the r-f generator, the r-f voltage across the LC tank will decrease —how much it decreases depends on how close the metallic object is to L.

The r-f voltage developed across the LC circuit can be amplified, rectified, and used to operate a relay. The sensitivity of this circuit is mainly dependent on the Q of the LC circuit; the higher the Q, the greater the sensitivity. Also, sensitivity can be increased as the outside diameter of search coil L is increased.

While a signal generator is shown as the r-f signal source in Fig. 6-14, a fixed-frequency oscillator can be substituted. It is recommended that a crystal oscillator be used for maximum oscillator stability, since any drift in the oscillator frequency will appear the same as a metallic object approaching the search coil.

A typical 100-kc crystal oscillator circuit is shown in Fig. 6-15. The pictorial diagram in Fig. 6-16 is a good arrangement for this circuit.

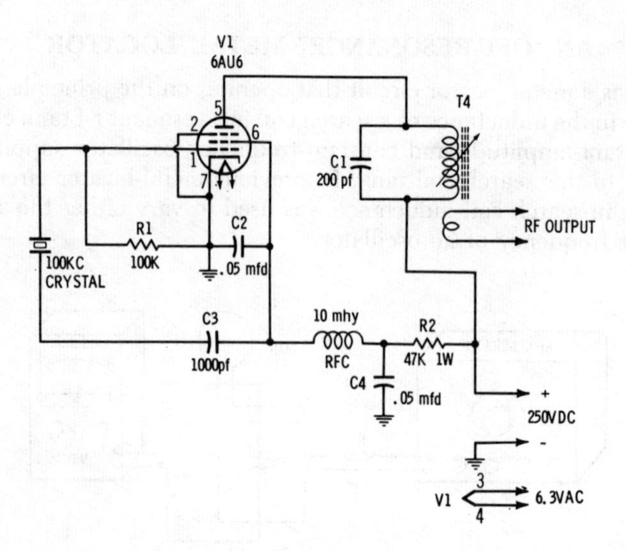

Fig. 6-15. A 100-kc crystal oscillator for use with Fig. 6-14.

Parts List for Fig. 6-15

Item	Description
C1	Capacitor, 200 pf, mica
C2, C4	Caparitors, .05 mfd, paper, Goodall 663UW or equiv.
C3	Capacitor, 1000 pf, mica
R1	Resistor, 100K, ½ watt
R2	Resistor, 47K, 1 watt
RFC	Choke, 10 mh, r-f
T4	Transformer, r-f, secondary winding consists of 25 turns of no. 30 enameled wire wound on the unoccupied part of the coil form on a J.W. Miller no. 6314 coil, or equiv.
V1	Tube, 6AU6
X1	Crystal, 100 kc, James Knight H93 or equiv.

This circuit is relatively simple and will give good results with any of the 100-kc crystals on the market. When the circuit (less the r-f signal generator) of Fig. 6-14 is used with this crystal oscillator, the values of L and C are selected to resonate at 100 kc. It is difficult to give specific values here, since they depend on the final outside diameter of the search coil. The best approach is to first wind the search coil, then place various values of capacitance across the coil until the combination resonates at 100 kc. Perhaps the simplest way

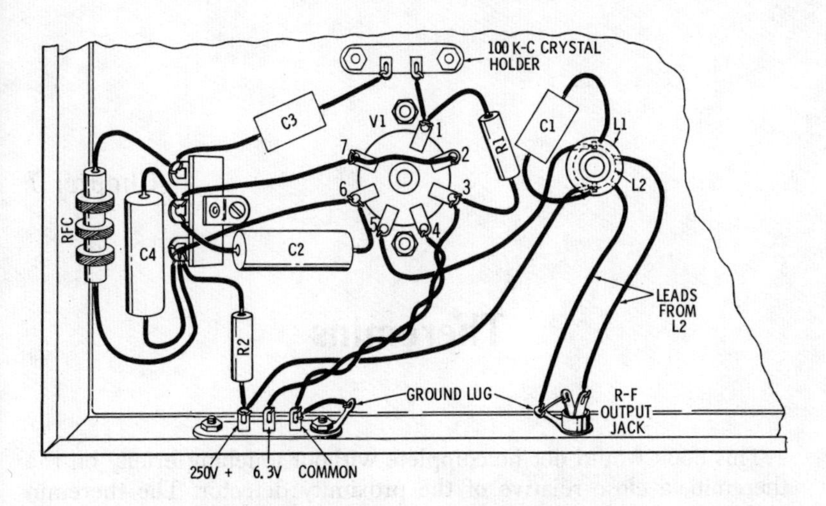

Fig. 6-16. Pictorial diagram for Fig. 6-15.

of doing this is to parallel the coil with a 365 picofarad variable capacitor and then adjust the capacitor until 100-kc resonance is obtained. Depending on the search coil used, it may be necessary to add additional fixed capacitance in parallel with the variable capacitor to obtain the 100-kc resonance.

Chapter 7

Theremins

This book would not be complete without touching briefly on the theremin, a close relative of the proximity detector. The theremin is the source of those eerie sounds you hear in science fiction movies and on TV, and it has become popular as a conversation piece in the home. While it is possible to obtain real music from a theremin once its operation is mastered, they are most generally used to produce "out of this world" music and sound effects. The theremin is based on the principle that a change in the capacitance of a variable-frequency oscillator (vfo) will produce a change in the heterodyne output signal of this oscillator and a fixed-frequency oscillator. In the pages that follow, you will examine several practical theremin circuits.

A TWO-STAGE THEREMIN

Fig. 7-1 is the schematic of a simple vacuum-tube theremin which will serve to introduce you to the remarkable world of theremin music. The circuit is straightforward, and only a few, inexpensive components are used in its construction.

As you can see, the basic circuit is very similar to the beat-frequency proximity detector described in Chapter 3 (Fig. 3-1), except that an audio amplifier is substituted for the voltage-doubler rectifier and relay control stage. Also, the theremin uses a different type of carrier frequency filter. The vfo consists of V1, L1, C1, C3, C6, and R1. The fixed-frequency oscillator consists of V2A, L2, C2, C4, C7, and R2.

In operation, L1 and L2 are adjusted so that the frequency difference between the two oscillators is about 1 kc, without an object near the pitch plate. Since the outputs of the two oscillators heterodyne in V1, the resulting 1000-cps beat-frequency is developed at the plate of V1. The output of V1 is filtered and amplified to feed a speaker.

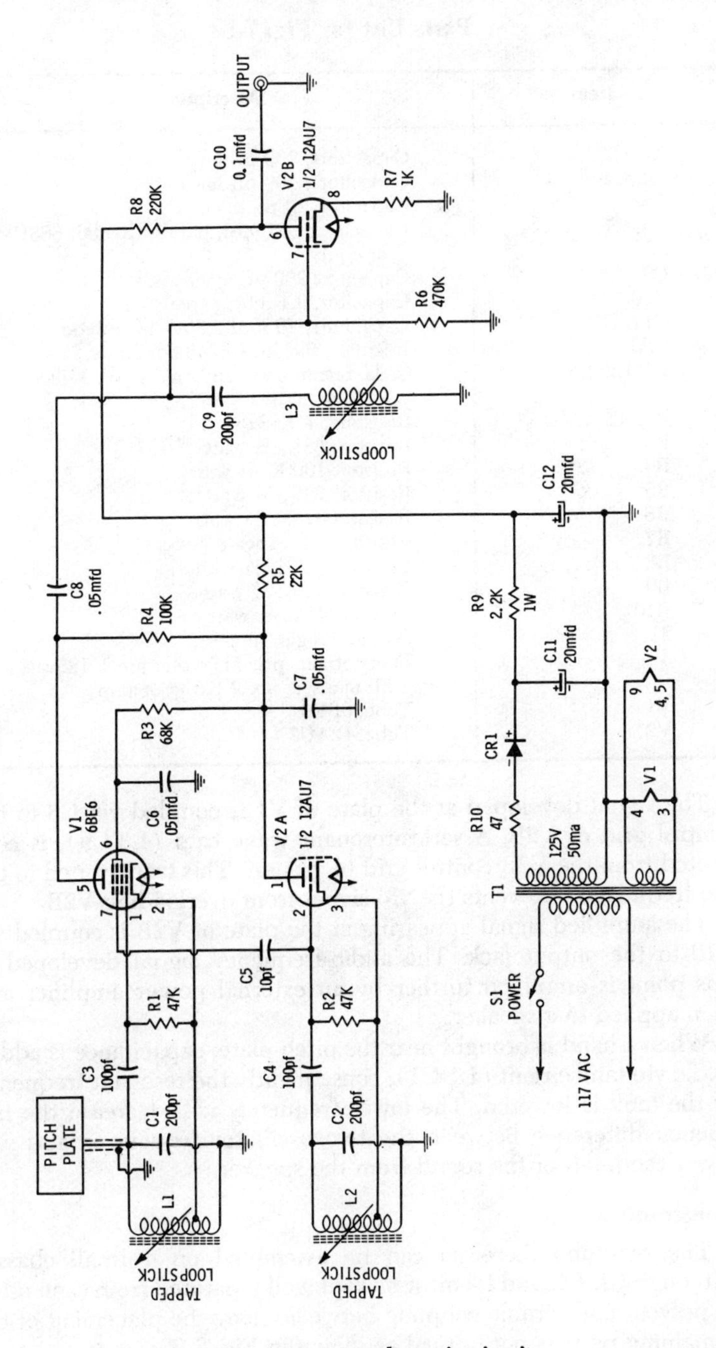

Fig. 7-1. A two-stage theremin circuit.

Parts List for Fig. 7-1

Item	Description
C1, C2	Capacitors, 200 pf, mica
C3, C4	Capacitors, 100 pf, mica
C5	Capacitor, 10 pf, mica
C6, C7, C8	Capacitors, .05 mfd, paper, Goodall 663UW or equiv.
C9	Capacitor, 200 pf, mica
C10	Capacitor, 0.1 mfd, paper
C11, C12	Capacitors, 20 mfd, 250v electrolytic
CR1	Rectifier, silicon, 1N2484 or equiv.
L1, L2, L3	Coils, ferrite core, antenna, J. W. Miller 9012 or equiv.
R1, R2	Resistors, 47K, ½ watt
R3	Resistor, 68K, ½ watt
R4	Resistor, 100 K, ½ watt
R5	Resistor, 22K, ½ watt
R6	Resistor, 470K, ½ watt
R7	Resistor, 1K, ½ watt
R8	Resistor, 220K, ½ watt
R9	Resistor, 2.2K, ½ watt
R10	Resistor, 47K, ½ watt
S1	Switch, toggle, spst
T1	Transformer, pri. 117v sec. no. 1 125v @ 50 ma, sec. no. 2 6.3 @ 2 amp
V1	Tube, 6BE6
V2	Tube, 12AU7

The signal developed at the plate of V1 is coupled via C8 to the control grid of V2B. A series-resonant wave trap (L3-C9), is connected from the V2B control grid to ground. This trap (tuned to the vfo frequency) prevents the vfo signal from overloading V2B.

The amplified signal appearing at the plate of V2B is coupled via C10 to the output jack. The audio-frequency signal developed at this point is amplified further by an external power amplifier and then applied to a speaker.

When a hand is brought near the pitch plate, capacitance is added to the vfo tank circuit (L1-C1); consequently the resonant frequency of the tank is lowered. The lower frequency will decrease the frequency difference between the two oscillator frquencies and will lower the pitch of the sound from the speaker.

Construction

The two-tube theremin can be assembled on a small chassis. Although L1, L2, and L3 must be kept well separated from each other to prevent undesirable coupling between them, the placement of the remaining parts is not critical as shown in Fig. 7-2.

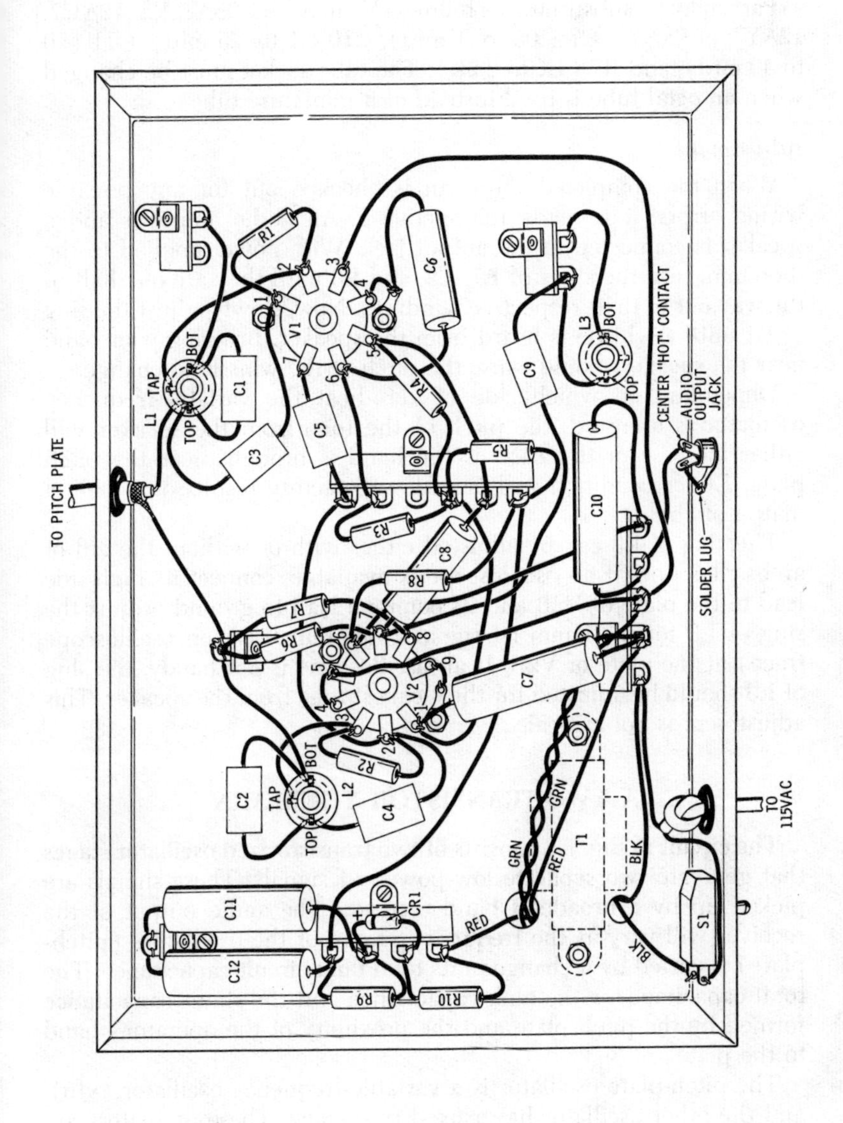

Fig. 7-2. Pictorial diagram for Fig. 7-1.

The pitch plate can be any convenient size or shape, (for example, a 6 inch × 6 inch square), or a large piece of wire can be used instead of the plate.

Parts may be substituted as follows: V1 may be a 6SA7, V2 (12AU7, 12AY7, or 6SN7), C7 (.05 to .1 mfd), C10 (.1 to .25 mfd), C11 (20 to 40 mfd), and R7 (1K to 2.2K). The tube socket must be changed when an octal tube is used instead of a miniature tube.

Adjustment

When the completed theremin is checked out for any possible wiring errors, it is ready for operation. An audio amplifier and a speaker is connected to the output jack. With power applied to the theremin, turn the slugs of L1, L2, and L3 until they are one half of the way out of their respective windings. Now, slowly adjust the slug of L1 until a whistle is heard from the speaker. Bringing your hand near the speaker should cause the pitch of the whistle to change.

Depending on which side of zero-beat the variable-frequency oscillator is adjusted, the pitch of the tone from the speaker will either increase or decrease as the hand is brought near the pitch plate. Either condition will provide satisfactory results; it is only a matter of choice.

The slug of L3 can be adjusted either with or without the aid of an oscilloscope. If an oscilloscope is available, connect its high-side lead to the plate of V2B and its common lead to ground. Adjust the slug of L3 for minimum r-f signal (minimum hash on oscilloscope trace) at the plate of V2B. If an oscilloscope is not handy, the slug of L3 should be adjusted for the cleanest tone from the speaker. This adjustment is not critical.

A TWO-TRANSISTOR THEREMIN

The circuit in Fig. 7-3 consists of two transistorized oscillator stages that generate two separate low-power r-f signals. These signals are picked up by a broadcast band receiver. The audio output of the receiver will vary as the frequency of one of the oscillators (pitch-plate) is varied by a change in its total tank-circuit capacitance. The total capacitance is the tank capacitance and the shunt capacitance formed by the pitch plate and the proximity of the operator's hand to the plate.

The pitch-plate oscillator is a variable-frequency oscillator (vfo), and the other oscillator has a fixed frequency. These oscillators are separately tuned (without an object in the vicinity of the pitch plate) for two different frequencies. The vfo oscillator is tuned so that its output frequency is 1 kc higher or lower than that of the fixed oscillator and so it does not fall on the frequency of a local a-m station.

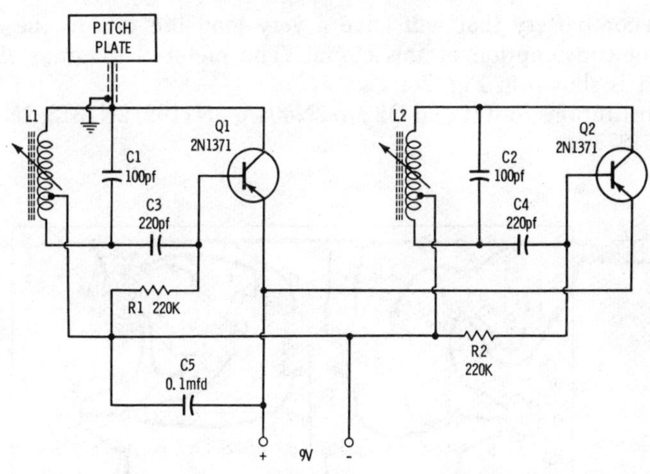

Fig. 7-3. A two-transistor theremin circuit.

Parts List for Fig. 7-3

Item	Description
C1	Capacitor, 100 pf, mica
C2	Capacitor, 100 pf, mica
C3	Capacitor, 220 pf, mica
C4	Capacitor, 220 pf, mica
C5	Capacitor, 0.1 mfd, paper or disc
Q1, Q2	Transistors, 2N1371
R1, R2	Resistors, 220, ½ watt
L1, L2	Coils, ferrite core, J. W. Miller no. 9012, or equiv.

The pitch oscillator (vfo) consists of Q1, L1, C1, C3, and R1, and the fixed oscillator consists of Q2, L2, C2, C4, and R2. C5 is an r-f bypass capacitor. Both the circuits are Hartley oscillators.

When your hand is brought near the pitch plate, more capacitance is added across the pitch-oscillator tank circuit (L1-C1), thus lowering the frequency of tank. This will change the pitch of the tone heard from the radio speaker.

Construction

The two-oscillator portion of the theremin can be assembled on a small piece of perforated phenolic board. Terminals inserted through the phenolic board are used as tie-points for the various components.

Component layout is not critical, except L1 and L2 should be fairly well separated to avoid interaction. Power is supplied by a 9-volt transistor battery that will have a very long life due to the small current consumption of this circuit. The pictorial diagram of this circuit is shown in Fig. 7-4.

Substitutions for Q1 and Q2 are 2N404A, 2N1192, 2N1373, 2N1375, or 2N1377.

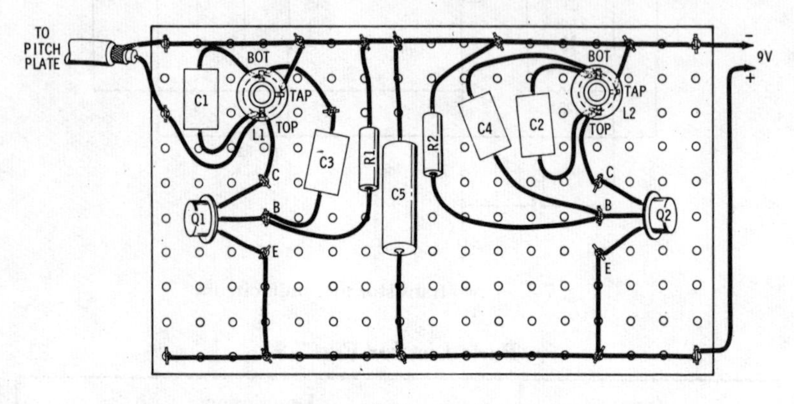

Fig. 7-4. Pictorial diagram for Fig. 7-3.

Adjustment

When the theremin is completed, connect a 9-volt battery to its positive and negative terminals and place the theremin chassis several inches from an a-m broadcast band radio. Turn the tuning slug of L1 until it is approximately two thirds of the way out of its respective winding and the slug of L2 until it is approximately one third of the way out of its winding. Slowly turn the dial of the radio until either oscillator signal is heard. The signal can be identified by either a whistle if it is "on top" of a broadcast station, or as a "quieting" of the receiver background noise—L1 or L2 should be adjusted until this latter point on dial is reached. You can determine which oscillator is being received by adjusting L1 then L2. The "quieting" frequency point is the desired tuning point on the dial. If turning the slug of L1 causes a shift in the "quieting point" on the radio-receiver tuning dial, then it is the vfo signal that is being received on the radio. If the slug of L2 causes the shift in the dial setting, then the fixed oscillator is being received. After establishing which oscillator is the source of the received "quieting" signal, adjust the slug of the other oscillator until a whistle is heard from the speaker. Bringing your hand near the pitch plate should now cause the pitch of the sound to change.